3 - 4 - 57

CE

PADEREWSKI

PADEREWSKI

by Charlotte Kellogg

NEW YORK   THE VIKING PRESS   1956

Typography by Charles E. Skaggs

PRINTED IN THE U.S.A. BY THE VAIL-BALLOU PRESS

TO
Jean Kellogg

Contents

PART ONE

CHAPTER I

Warsaw Conservatory

Young Ignace Paderewski helped his father with the chest as they dropped down from freight car to platform. Everywhere he saw Russian uniforms, for he and his father were still in the part of Poland that Russia ruled. All the way from the village of Sudylkow, on the southeastern borderland, to Warsaw, the capital, the train had run across rich plains. This land had been seized more than a century ago, when Germany, Austria, and Russia had carved up Poland, each taking about a third. Beneath the Paderewskis' joy in being able to travel lay that dark knowledge.

While they looked for a carriage to take them to a hotel, Ignace caught glimpses of one of the bridges that span the wide Vistula. Warsaw had grown beside this river, which carries boats and goods to and from the Baltic Sea. Now, as the low, open carriage rattled through the crowds along narrow, stone-paved streets lined by exciting shop windows, he turned to his father. "What fun to jump out and see these shops on foot!"

His father smiled. "More fun if we had money. You'll find traders here from all over the world."

Ignace leaned out. On both sides of the street he saw fascinating displays, from cheeses, sausages, and fish to musical instruments, statues, and ornaments of carved wood, painted boxes and candlesticks, bright linens and ribbons. "Antonina would like that," he said, pointing to a blue shawl patterned with field flowers.

It hadn't been easy to leave his sister. For a long time they had had no other companions as they ran about the stream-crossed fields that were red with wild strawberries and poppies. Antonina was fourteen, two years older than Ignace, and had been mother as well as sister to him, for their mother had died soon after he was born. "Little Mother Antonina" Jan, their father, called her. That morning she had stood apart from all the shouting, singing relatives and friends who had gathered to see them off, and then, though she was crying, as Ignace knew, she waved gaily until his answering signals and the train disappeared over the steppes.

Now Ignace saw wider streets, flanked by handsome gray stone houses; he and his father drove past parks bright with children, looked up at spires of Western churches and domes of Eastern Orthodox ones. By the time the driver reined his horse before a small hotel popular with visitors from the borderlands, Ignace had a thrilling impression of the city where, if all went well, he was to live.

They had to concentrate at once on their three main problems: arranging for Ignace's admission to the Warsaw Conservatory, buying a piano, and finding him a place to live. Jan wished he felt more certain that country lessons could prepare a student for the entrance examinations of one of Europe's foremost conservatories. Ever since his son, when scarcely more than a baby, had begun to pick out beautiful tones and melodies on their rickety piano, he had been convinced that the boy had talent and must have a chance to develop it. But the trip to Warsaw with horses cost so much that he hadn't been able to afford it, and there would have been expenses to follow. Instead of trying to send the boy to the city to study, he had engaged the best teachers he could find in the region—first a violinist, then a pianist from farther away, who stayed several days at lesson times, but who was not, as his pupil was to learn, the teacher he needed.

As they neared the famous old school, Ignace grew tense and nervous, trying to imagine what the director would be like, and the examinations, and wondering if his compositions would help (they had brought with them the large copybook his father had made several years ago to spur him to compose). Yet, though anxious, he had too, as he was to have throughout his life, a belief in what he must do, stronger than doubt and anxiety. Some would call it a belief in his destiny.

Director Kontski may have sensed that deep certainty during their first meeting in his office. At its close he told Jan Paderewski to worry no longer, for his son would be admitted to the conservatory, without examinations!

Ignace ran down the steps and threw his hat in the air. Then they joyously set out to look for a piano. The first search was discouraging. They tramped from one shop to another; the pianos were either too poor or too high-priced. Jan Paderewski and his son hesitated to visit the important Kerntopf piano center, fearing to find nothing within their means. But in the end they climbed the stairs to this rambling factory, on the floor that served also as family living quarters. There spread a sea of pianos.

Ignace's fingers tingled at the sight of the gleaming keyboards. "Might I try one?"

"Of course, son." The kindly piano maker seemed to like the looks of this boy. "Help yourself."

While his father explained why they had come, Ignace found a stool, sat down, and soon forgot everything but the piano. How different from any other he had played! What tones!

The price was high; yet how long could their search go on? Jan Paderewski decided to buy one of these pianos, and was arranging to do so when he was interrupted by Mr. Kerntopf's eldest son, Edward, a young man in his twenties. He had been listening to the playing and also to the conversation between the fathers.

"Why buy a piano when we can easily lend your boy one for as long a time as he will need it?" Edward said.

This was unbelievable. Was everything to be so easily arranged—first no conservatory examinations, now the loan of a piano? To Ignace these events, this sea of pianos, seemed miraculous. And more luck was to follow.

Jan Paderewski, finding the Kerntopfs so intelligent and friendly, asked if they could suggest a suitable place for his son to live while attending the conservatory. "Why couldn't he join our large family?" Edward asked quietly, as if this were only a natural question. "There's room, and the cost would be little." He called Ignace and clapped him on the shoulder. "Wouldn't you like to come here to live, young man, and"—he laughed—"have all these pianos to practice on?"

Ignace looked up at him, so happy, so moved that he could

scarcely reply. "I would," he said simply. Edward understood.

There was no doubting the warmth of the invitation. Jan Paderewski was overwhelmed. "After all my worries about settling my son in Warsaw," he said, "I find no words to thank you."

They went back to their hotel, to return the following day with the chest containing Ignace's belongings.

That was the fairy-story side of this experience. It didn't prevent Ignace's having a pretty hard time when, after being shown his space in the room shared by four Kerntopf boys, he suddenly realized that his father was going back to the country, to Antonina, the horses and dogs, the cherry trees, the fields. A wave of terrible homesickness swept over him; he couldn't choke back sobs.

Motherly Mrs. Kerntopf put her arms about him. "Now, don't feel so bad, though it's only natural you should. The boys and their sisters will make you see that you're not a stranger in a strange city, but just one of a big family, who belongs here."

Indeed, there was little room for homesickness at the Kerntopf factory, with its busy workmen and teasing troop of ten boys and girls. The family's generous way of living was not only a happy one for themselves; it attracted many people to them. Ignace soon found that this was a favorite meeting place for Warsaw musicians and for many musicians from other countries who came to give concerts or stopped en route to or from the Russian court at Saint Petersburg.

After school or between long practice hours on a chosen piano Edward was apt to call, "Clean up, come along," and whisk him off to a concert hall, or the opera house, where one of the Kerntopf intimates was the conductor. There Ignace first heard Rossini's *Barber of Seville*, Bellini's *Norma* —from which he and Antonina had had to learn boring duets —Verdi operas, the lovely *Aida* among them, and Polish music, which thrilled him most. After such performances he could scarcely control his excitement. He felt a flame burning within him. He himself would write a symphony, an opera, embodying in them Polish tunes he had heard country people sing and play for dancing as long as he could remember.

Edward arranged too for him to play before musicians, and asked for their opinion of his playing. If all this looked like a heavy program for a boy just turned thirteen, the Kerntopfs understood how normal it was to a boy of his gifts. Besides, they knew that he was, in free hours, even more lively and mischievous at home than he was reported to be at school.

Once Mr. Kerntopf had taken him to a certain music teacher to get a verdict on his talent. While the two men were conversing. Ignace was left to busy himself with some music sheets. When the teacher asked young Paderewski to play, the boy went to the piano and executed a brilliant polonaise.

"Splendid! This boy has genius," the master exclaimed. "Whose music is it?"

"I think it is an Oginski polonaise," said Ignace. "It is an air well known in our home district."

After leaving the house, Mr. Kerntopf asked him how he liked the teacher.

"I liked him much, but—"

"But what?"

He giggled. "Well—he doesn't know what an Oginski polonaise is."

"Why are you laughing? He praised you beautifully."

"Yes, but while you were talking, I read over his own polonaise—"

"Well?"

"It was that I played for him, with variations."[1]

Because of his ruddy hair and nimble feet his schoolmates quickly gave Ignace the nickname Squirrel. He had already found his particular student friend, another Ignace, two years older, who was studying violin. There was scarcely a day without a laugh over some escapade of theirs. For Ignace Paderewski, relaxing fun was necessary. His class and study periods were long. Teachers who saw a big future ahead pressed him hard—especially those who were masters in theory—in counterpoint and all that concerned composition.

Because of his success in these classes one might have expected him to be satisfied. But he was not learning what he needed most to know: the science of piano playing—such things as correct fingering and pedaling. More than discouraging was his first experience in a piano class. "Not hands for playing," the teacher declared. "That thumb, that third finger, too short." He gave Ignace a trial, then told him to leave, to take up some other instrument.

This Ignace did; he entered another class, with the same

[1] Adapted from *Paderewski, the Story of a Modern Immortal,* by Charles Phillips. New York, The Macmillan Company, 1934.

result. "You have no talent for the flute. Choose something else."

He passed from clarinet to oboe to trombone. His trombone teacher was enthusiastic. He advised Ignace to stick to the trombone, which he was now playing in the school band. Ignace realized that the more he knew about all the instruments, the less difficulty he would have in writing orchestral music. But he wanted to play the piano! Sometimes he felt dismally that, in spite of all the drudgery, he was moving from failure to failure.

At those times it was good to hear Edward's "You will be a great pianist—never doubt it!" or to be taken to a glorious concert, or just to be left alone at the piano on the factory floor, to improvise hour after hour. At last his iron persistence won, and he began to make progress in his piano classes.

He found his best rest and inspiration when he wandered about the city, looking at buildings and monuments—reminders of Poland's great past—or walked through the park near the Belvedere Palace—once the home of Poland's kings —or lingered to enjoy the yellow-walled Zamek. He saw this palace often because it was near his favorite statue of King Sigismund III. The figure of Sigismund stood on top of a column, high in air, holding a cross in one hand and a sword in the other. All Poles in Warsaw, and most other Poles, knew the saying, "When Sigismund shakes his sword, then Poland will become free." Many believed it. As Ignace looked up at the statue and remembered that legend, he could not foresee how, strangely, history would prove it true.

He went often to churches, not only to pray but to visit shrines of heroes and saints. These churches were open all day; he could go inside on his way to or from the conservatory. His favorite place to visit was the seventeenth-century Church of the Holy Cross, in the crypt of which the heart of Chopin is buried. Kneeling before this shrine, he would repeat the promise to live for Poland and for music. He renewed this promise one day when Edward said, "Now for a real excursion, Squirrel," and took him to a small, tree-shaded house in the country, where, on February 22, 1810 (about fifty years before his own birth), Chopin was born.

At school he did not manage himself so well. True, his escapades were not disastrous; he did work until his back ached and his hands felt as if they would drop off. He did continue to win brilliant successes in certain classes. But for other reasons he got into trouble, and at last into rather serious trouble. The conservatory director wished to organize a student orchestra for Warsaw, which had no regular one. Ignace was named first-trombone player. Exams were just ahead; the boy couldn't bring himself to give up vital study time for rehearsals. How would his father feel if he didn't pass, if he repaid such kindness with failure? The director insisted that he come to rehearsals and on time.

Then one day there was an unpleasant scene. "It is unjust. I will not stay," Ignace objected, when told that he must remain after school as punishment for not attending a rehearsal.

The director determined to settle this revolt (other students had taken a like stand) then and there. "But you shall remain."

Ignace tried to walk out of the room, was stopped, but in the end did go, and was promptly suspended. This greatly upset the Kerntopfs—all except Edward, who sided with

Ignace. "He is right. The director was wrong in forcing him to give up study hours to the orchestra."

Fortunately some of the faculty felt the same way; and though they did not approve Ignace's hot-headedness, they worked to get him back. Finally word came that he could return. And glad he was to do so, and to pass his exams. The Kerntopf family, immensely relieved, didn't guess that this crisis had not ended. It flared again, with Ignace and a few other students at its rebellious center. For the second time he had to climb the piano-factory stairs to tell his friends that he had been suspended. And after that he had to get along as best he could, taking a few private lessons from a conservatory professor, practicing alone, and giving lessons to young pupils at twelve cents an hour, to make minor expenses. His father continued to pay his board and provide for major necessities.

After about a year he was readmitted to the conservatory, where he and his friend, violinist Ignace, put their heads together in a bit of daring planning.

"Why wait till we're older?" the violinist argued. "We've enough pieces ready to make a good program. You have your Chopin numbers for a principal section, and I have plenty for my part."

"Yes, why not make a tour, and win fame and money? We could play first in smaller northern Polish towns and then move eastward into Russia."

They were for starting as soon as possible. Then an older classmate—a cellist—decided to join the venture. And, just as they were about to leave, the conservatory, surprisingly, endorsed the plan. They were elated. This approval would impress the public.

So, in summer weather, the three students, armed with cello and violin (they must find pianos on the spot), set out to conquer a bit of the world. Since they had no manager they would have to plan as they went—a precarious business.

In the beginning they scored some successes and made a little money. But there were few railroads; often they had to depend on broken-down wagons to take them from one town to the next. Lodgings were uncomfortable; there were days when they had not enough money for meals, and nights when they got no sleep. Worse still, they could scarcely practice because of the time it took to find a hall, the time lost in going from door to door before discovering someone willing to risk having his piano moved by such workmen as youths might collect. But through all sorts of uncertainties, including weather—for fall had come, with winter on the way—they pushed on, played to empty or filled houses, made or lost money, ate or went hungry, and slowly grew wiser.

The cellist was the first to give up. Like a sailor who does not trust the sky ahead, he turned back to port. That left the two Ignaces to go on alone. Fortunately they knew a trick that people who camp in mountains learn—putting newspapers under one's clothing to keep out cold. Otherwise, as they pressed into Russia, thinly clad, in below-zero weather, their plight would have been even worse than it was.

One morning, after they had been stranded for almost two weeks without money to pay for their room, with only enough for bread and tea, and when heavy snow was falling, violinist Ignace said, "You know how I hate to, but I've simply got to write to my parents for help."

"Write if you want to. I can't do that yet." Ignace shivered, bent over a table, his head in his hands.

When money came and they had paid the landlord, his partner decided to go no farther. Their adventure had lasted almost a year.

Still Ignace Paderewski wouldn't give up. Saint Petersburg would be different! Finally he too was forced to write his father for money. The letter bringing it urged him to come home. But he persisted stubbornly: Go home? Not until I play at least one successful concert in Saint Petersburg.

There a scoundrel managed to make off with his money, and a second stole his luggage. Ignace had no one to turn to. But a kind-hearted plumber saw him tramping the streets and shared his own miserable quarters and scant food with the boy. Ignace's body and spirit were exhausted; the best he could now hope for was to get back to Sudylkow alive.

This, because of Jan Paderewski's great anxiety, he managed to do. For like something dropped from the sky came another letter, with sufficient money for his return. In later years he liked to recall that blessed homecoming, when his father and Antonina met him with no complaint, only thankful that he was safely home. He swiftly determined to reward this generous love by finishing the remaining work of the two-year course in record time.

He worked day and night and got his degree in six months. At the graduation exercises he played the Grieg Piano Concerto in A Minor. And his father heard the director say, as he handed Ignace the conservatory diploma, "Of all the class, Ignace Paderewski has won the highest honors."

CHAPTER II

Berlin and the
Tatra Mountains

WHEN Helena Modjeska, Polish "queen of the stage," came to Warsaw, conservatory students always crowded to see her; nothing so fired their ambition as did her acting. With the others, Ignace saved to buy tickets, saw her first as Ophelia and heard the *Hamlet* music, written by Moniuszko, a Pole, that accompanied the play. He clapped and shouted for her and for Poland, and showered her with flowers. Russian officials did not like these scenes but for some reason did not interfere. Ignace wasn't yet a friend of Modjeska, but he had heard much about her; he knew that people were urging her to learn English and to visit the United States, where a golden future waited for all, particularly for artists. This vision and hope helped many a boy to stick at a grinding task.

Ignace now possessed a conservatory diploma, which he stored in the chest in the room he still shared on the piano-factory floor. Mrs. Kerntopf, Edward, and all the other Kerntopfs seemed as pleased as his own family over his having at last passed this milestone. But to him the degree represented preparation, not so much completed as just begun—a first step taken. He was burning to take the next step. Some of Europe's best teachers lived in Berlin; he wanted now to study composition with the famous Professor Friedrich Kiel, to learn all there was to know about composition.

Some of Ignace's compositions had won success, and people seemed ready enough to believe in his future as a composer.

"But what's the use of talking about it?" he said to Edward one day, as they were on their way to church. "I haven't the money even for a ticket to Berlin."

"No," Edward admitted, "but you'll get it."

"If I earn it. Father can't do more. I'll *have* to teach!" He threw up his hands and made a wry face, and they laughed. Edward knew how little Ignace wanted to teach. "When I want only to be taught! But still I'm lucky. I won't have to wear out shoes in looking for a job. I can take the one at the school."

Immediately after his graduation the conservatory had offered him a place on its staff, poorly paid but at least a beginning. He could stretch the meager salary by giving private lessons. He postponed going to Berlin and accepted the conservatory post. He must have been a good teacher, because his pupils did well. And though he was terribly tired at the end of the day, he still managed to practice and to compose.

Then life suddenly whirled up to a different level—one of mysterious happiness. A lovely young girl with the same name as his sister had come to the conservatory. Antonina Korsak was not only beautiful but gifted, and she intensely believed in Ignace's talents. They fell in love and quickly married.

Ignace plunged into more work in order to earn the rent

for their tiny apartment and make a comfortable living for his wife. In their idyllic partnership he was continually discovering some new beauty in her nature, as she was in his. Then, after a brief year together, Antonina died, leaving him with a baby boy to care for. As Ignace knelt beside the bed, praying, he tried to comfort the crying baby in his arms. "Poor little one, motherless as I was, may God help me to be as good a father to you as mine is to me."

It was arranged that Antonina's mother would take care of the baby so that Ignace could give up his teaching job and go to Berlin, where he could have the superior training that would advance his career. The German capital was only a few hours west of Warsaw, but farther west than he had yet been, and only during the frightful Saint Petersburg experience had he seen so large a city. He was impressed by its orderly appearance, its parks along the river; by the way the crowds seemed to be always excitedly talking about the last Wagner opera they had heard. But he did not like Berlin very well; and the people of Berlin showed no love for Poles. He had no desire to share in the boisterous life of the students, young men from all over the world; he wanted only to make every lesson count. But his professor advised him, as earlier ones had done, to study, not the piano, but another instrument— this time, the violin! And he added the likewise familiar comment that Ignace showed unusual talent for composition. The young student now worked so many hours a day that his face was distressingly pale beneath the shock of ruddy hair. Often he looked almost ill. Yet, even so, he found time to meet important men in the music world and to make new friends. Those who knew him might argue that he lacked this or that quality, but all agreed that he had a special gift for making friends.

Foremost among his Berlin friends was the great composer Richard Strauss. Ignace had his best times with the Strauss family. The children of the household adored the young man who played Polish polkas and mazurkas for them and told them lively stories of his homeland. Some day I will tell them to my boy, he thought. He always regarded Richard Strauss as his favorite modern composer.

Altogether he spent two years of tremendous work in Berlin. His stay there was broken only by a return to Warsaw to see his little son Alfred and to rest and earn more money for the baby's needs and his own. How did he rest? He taught at the conservatory and gave private lessons; at night he took lessons himself in history, mathematics, Latin, and literature, and, on the side, studied the cello!

Besides all this he gave a few concerts, one of them unique. He laughed heartily later when he described it—as he did many times, for friends were apt to beg for this story. It happened in a country town, where he went on a tour to play accompaniments for the violinist Ladislas Gorski, as he was often invited to do because he read music so quickly. In addition he was to give several piano numbers.

Luckily a young student asked to go along. After they reached the town at about the concert hour and found no piano in the shabby hall, he and the student raced up and down streets, knocking at doors, appealing for the loan of one. Finally someone offered an upright that looked as if it wouldn't hold together until it reached the platform. How they finally moved this old case, with Paderewski, his mop of hair damp with perspiration, running circles around it, made a good story in itself.

Only a few minutes before the concert was to begin he sat down to try the keys. The hammers rose, but many did not come down, for they were stuck in mid-air!

"This is terrible! We can't give the concert. Look!" He struck other keys.

It was then that the student went into action. He moved close to the piano.

"Try again!" he said. At the instant a hammer stuck, he pushed it down. Faster and faster Ignace played; more and more swiftly, back and forth, sped the hands of the young man behind the piano. A mad scene, and the audience was arriving! The violinist began his performance; while he played it was easier to conceal what was happening. But by the time the pianist was finishing his first solo, people were fascinated; they stood up, eyes not on him but on the whirlwind artist at the rear of the piano. Somehow the three desperate performers finished that program.

After the study in Berlin with Kiel, in composition, and later with Kiel's pupil, Professor Heinrich Urban, in orchestration, one thing was completely clear in Paderewski's mind. He had learned what he most needed to know about the writing of music. From now on no one could discourage him from learning other things he was determined to discover. He would let nothing, *nothing*, prevent his mastering the art of piano playing.

But first he must rest. And where in Poland was there a lovelier vacation place than the Tatra mountains in the south? He chose the little town of Zakopane, where the stream is loud and the air sweet with larch fragrance. There are few mountain towns anywhere so picturesque as this Polish one, where almost every cottage is a center for wood-carving or for flowery lacemaking, and where the gaily costumed peasants make the streets look like painted pictures.

Besides, he had long wanted to hear these peasants sing, and to watch their dances so that he could introduce their tunes and rhythms into his music, as Chopin had done. But he little dreamed what help awaited him in this search. Just after he arrived in Zakopane he met an elderly man, Doctor Chalubinski, whom all the peasants loved, who knew best which ones sang the loveliest old tunes or danced the most beautiful mazurkas and polonaises.

Nor did he guess what other good fortune waited at Zakopane. For there lived Helena Modjeska and her husband; Modjeska, adored by all the theater world and just re-turned from a triumphant Shakespeare tour in the United States! San Franciscans, crowding to hear her play Lady Macbeth, had lost their hearts to this gorgeous woman with long braids and fabulous eyes, who moved like a flame. She in turn had fallen in love with California, and planned to found a Polish colony there.

One day in the village the old doctor said to Paderewski, "You must come with me," and forthwith introduced him to Modjeska. She at once asked him to play. Here was a scene to stir the pride of any nation: the young musician, tall, rather frail, blue-eyed, his hair more red than gold, the fair Polish type, his sensitive face flushed as he sat at the piano, playing his compositions; beside him the older, dark-eyed, dark-haired, gloriously gifted actress, listening. Her face kindled with feeling as she realized that through this gifted youth at the piano the soul of Poland would once again speak to the whole world.

Modjeska's swift words of understanding and confidence meant everything to Ignace. Often he played for her; often they talked late into the night. Those compositions into which he was now weaving mountain tunes and rhythms, which were to be published as the *Tatra Album,* had a piercing beauty. Modjeska was convinced that he was ready to begin a concert career.

But he knew better. "Oh, no, not yet," he said. "In spite of all my effort I do not yet know how to use my hands. I want first to go to Vienna to study with the best piano teacher, with Leschetizky; I am planning to give a concert in Krakow to make enough money to begin."

Modjeska knew all about Leschetizky; he too was a Pole known round the world. She agreed that this was wise planning. But she did more. "I will go with you to Krakow, and recite poems at your concert. We will do it together."

What was she saying? A concert with Modjeska! He couldn't speak. His eyes flashed his gratitude. He saw every seat sold . . . crowds turned away . . .

CHAPTER III

Vienna Debut

K RAKOW, north of Zakopane, was Poland's capital long before Warsaw, the third capital, was chosen. It was a more beautiful capital, set in a region of rolling hills. "Pearl of Poland," people called it. Early on the day of the concert, the lines of eager purchasers began to form at the box office. By night a lively crowd was milling around the hall. It was interesting enough that a romantic-looking young Pole, whom some already called a second Chopin, was to play; but Modjeska was to recite poems! They shouted "Modjeska!" and clamored for tickets.

This audience was prepared for matchless recitations from her, but never had she shaken them as with that night's selections from Polish poets—from Mickiewicz, their greatest, from Slowacki and others—verses that set before their eyes, like a star in the night sky, the goal of Poland's liberation. They felt that she was not only calling to them to rededicate themselves, but that she called with passionate confidence to the young pianist. That confidence steadied him when he went to the piano; after a brief nervousness he forgot everything but Chopin, as he revealed a vigor, a positive statement in these compositions that was new to most of them. No wonder Modjeska believed in him. They stormed their approval.

The concert put two hundred dollars in Paderewski's pocket, which would pay for the trip to Vienna, for lessons from a famous teacher! The following day the two happy friends had time to look at Krakow before Ignace took the train to Warsaw. Along with the rest of Poland's history, he knew every page of Krakow's colorful past. But when he and Modjeska climbed the royal hill to visit the tombs of Poland's kings, when they knelt in the royal cathedral before the crucifix in front of which Jadwiga, Poland's girl queen, had knelt after she gave up family, lover, everything she had to give, to make a greater Poland, they could not forget that they did so only with the consent of the conqueror. Their thoughts, joyous after the concert success, became heavy, their faces darkly sad.

True, Zakopane and Krakow lay in the Austrian portion of Poland, and Austria treated Poles more liberally than did either Germany or Russia. But the fact remained that over all this jewel-bright country of their ancestors, Poland's for more than a thousand years, outsiders ruled. Paderewski told Modjeska how his father and all their family prayed and secretly worked for freedom; he told of a terrible night when Cossacks on horseback surrounded their house, searched for papers and weapons, took Jan off to prison, and then burned the whole village. Ignace had been only three at the time but he still felt the thong lash on his cheek in answer to his question, "What have you done with my father?" After that he and Antonina had lived with a good aunt until the authorities, two years later, released Jan, largely because the peasants gave them no peace till he was freed. Jan had found a house in another village, again got a job as administrator of an immense farm, with one thousand peasants working under his direction. Modjeska asked the young man to tell her more. He was glad to talk about his father, about how he hated war and was against all killing, yet how everyone knew there was no greater patriot than he; how nobles and peasants alike were always coming to him for advice. They liked the way he found time to carve little statues for the churches, to play his violin and to laugh with them over a comical happening or a witty saying.

But, as far as Modjeska could gather, neither Ignace's father nor his mother, the daughter of a Vilna University professor exiled to Siberia, had outstanding artistic talent, though many who had heard Ignace's mother greatly admired her playing.

"It was sad," she said, "that you couldn't know your mother. But you are lucky to know your father so well."

She was surprised to find how fluently Ignace already spoke French, Russian, German, Italian. "Your gift for languages will count in your work for our country," she said. "Oh, you will work!"

When they had reached the immense market place they looked up at the balcony of Saint Mary's Cathedral, from which on a silver horn a trumpeter still tells the hour, playing a tune that ends on a broken note—ends so in memory of a boy of medieval times whose life was broken off as he defended his church and his trumpet. To these two Poles, the younger and the older, as to no others of their day, the monuments of Krakow called.

And then Ignace was off for Vienna—off at last, he believed, to master the piano. One might have expected him to make an easy start, especially since Leschetizky's wife, an extremely popular pianist, already was playing one of his compositions on her programs—the Variations in A Minor—and had a fine opinion of the young composer.

But what passed between him and her husband as the elderly, bearded teacher looked him over and remembered that most successful pianists had begun their careers at the age of four or five? What could this Pole hope to do, Leschetizky thought, at this late day? There was kindly interest but no encouragement. Leschetizky repeated his terse judgment. "You have come too late."

This was hard to hear. It might have stopped another young man—but not Ignace. He couldn't turn the clock back to his boyhood, but he would prove that he could take instruction with a fresh mind and a will to learn. Leschetizky agreed to take him.

This meant that he had to begin at the beginning, go back to schoolboy exercises, Czerny's and others', which he and his sister had long practiced, after he had been teaching them to his own pupils. He had to unlearn faulty fingering and other bad habits of early years; it was much harder than if he were starting without previous study. It meant eight or ten hours of practice a day, sometimes even twelve. A pupil willing to work was the only pupil Leschetizky would accept.

Other teachers might offer quick methods, easy means to success; they might claim, for instance, that playing from the elbow instead of from the wrist, or holding the fingers stiffly instead of loosely, would assure a swift conquest of the piano. Vienna's great teacher made no such pleasant promises.

After a lesson a pupil often looked as if he had fought a battle. For Leschetizky the secret of learning a composition lay in studying slowly, patiently, it seemed forever, the first bar or phrase, until everything about it—fingering, accent, tone, above all pedaling—was mastered; then the next bar, the next, until the whole was built up, completely understood. Only then could one's playing have that crystal-clear quality it must have.

Students have described scenes in the Leschetizky classroom when one of them failed to reach the perfection of fingering, the singing tone, the rhythm, that his teacher insisted on. One reported rushing from the room, determined *never* to go back. Another wanted to break windows. Yet they did go back, to begin the struggle again. All knew that this iron master had a kind heart, that there was little he wouldn't do to help a student he believed in.

Leschetizky knew what it did for a music student to talk with a master in the music world. He arranged meetings with musicians, with Vienna's idol—Johannes Brahms of the magnificent symphonies, who asked Paderewski to play, and praised his work. After that Paderewski had many visits with Brahms. Thus hard, inspiring weeks passed. During them he learned more about how to play the piano than he had learned in all his previous study. But now his pockets were empty, even though he lived most simply in two plain rooms and was under no expense for lessons because from the beginning Leschetizky had refused to accept pay for teaching him. Once more he would have to teach. He returned to Warsaw.

Important things have a way of happening unexpectedly,

just as his meeting with Modjeska came about. We find him now in Warsaw, writing a piece that remains the most popular of all he wrote, the Minuet in G, and the account of how he happened to write it is one of the amusing stories he was asked to tell many times. When he arrived in Warsaw he found there the doctor who had been so kind to him in Zakopane; and often with the old man was an elderly friend, who was as fond of Mozart as the doctor was. If Paderewski dropped in of an evening, from the Kerntopfs', the two at once asked him to play again familiar Mozart scores. They wished nothing else—above all, no music of modern composers; no moderns could compare with the old ones.

As he invariably did, Paderewski thought of an amusing way to end a tiresome situation. He would write something in Mozart's manner, play it as if it were Mozart's own, and see what happened. As was his habit, he told no one of this plan but wrote the now famous Minuet. Soon he was playing it and watching the two old gentlemen out of the corner of his eye. They were delighted with the unfamiliar Mozart composition and asked him to play it again.

"But why have you not played this before?" they cried.

"Because I myself have just written it," he replied solemnly. At first they refused to believe him, and then seemed confused, angry, so mixed up in their minds about it that he was a bit ashamed of his successful joke. However, once the elderly gentlemen recovered, they did not resent it; nor has the world since!

Paderewski wasn't earning enough money in Warsaw, and had heartbreaking need for more. For infantile paralysis had

left his boy terribly crippled and it looked as if Alfred would
not walk again. He must find expert doctors. So, reluctantly,
he took a teaching job at the conservatory at Strasbourg, leading city of Alsace-Lorraine, once part of France. Leschetizky
had recommended him as the best-qualified young instructor
they could get. There he again made friends, several of whom
urged him not to wait but to try his luck immediately in
Paris.

"Not yet," he said, thanking them. He knew very well
where he was going as soon as his pockets were even partly
refilled—back to the grind with Leschetizky; to the eight-
to ten-hour days of fingering, pedaling, memorizing; to the
small plain rooms which, later on, when money poured into
the box offices, he was to try to buy because he wanted never
to lose them; and, he hoped, to a friend dear to him, though
unknown to others. For when he was about to leave for Warsaw and was practicing a Chopin study in thirds, his eye had
caught a fine silver thread dropped from the ceiling; down it
slid a tiny gray spider which hung motionless while he played.
Suddenly, when the music changed to sixths, that bright speck
raced up the thread to the ceiling. This fascinated him; would
the spider come down if he played thirds again? He played.
Down came the spider; it hung still, apparently listening.
Then, with the sixths, up again it shot. Over and over this
happened until he felt that here was the strangest friend he
had; he sensed a mysterious musical bond between them,
though he could not know what it was. When he had to
lock the door he hated to leave this marvelous, almost in-
visible companion. When he returned he stopped a moment

on the threshold. "Is it still here? Will it come down again?" He opened the piano, quickly played the thirds, watched. But the silver thread was gone. No spider came. He turned sadly to unpack his bags.[1]

When Paderewski played his Minuet, Leschetizky was tremendously enthusiastic. "This will become popular at once!" he said, and he was right. Soon one heard "The Paderewski Minuet" everywhere in Vienna; students too were always playing it. And then one day Leschetizky himself told Ignace that the time had come for him to make his debut. "I can arrange for you to play several numbers at a concert to be given by a well-liked Italian singer. The best-known musicians and critics of Vienna will be present."

Playing before an audience was no new experience for Ignace. From the days when country neighbors joined his father and sister and two grandfathers to listen to his improvising, the times he had played for few or many listeners had not been counted. But this was to be immensely more than just another concert. It was his bid for a place in the world of music, the test his father and Antonina and the Kerntopfs were sure he would pass. If he did, his career would have begun, the way would be opened to Paris, to the marvelous United States that Modjeska had so lately pictured. If he failed— He could not think what that would mean.

"Can I do it? Can I?" he asked himself. And that inner certainty that guided him replied, "You can." He would play, among other things, several Chopin compositions and

[1] Adapted from *Memoirs*, by Ignace Jan Paderewski and Mary Lawton. New York: Charles Scribner's Sons, 1939.

his own Variations and Fugue on an original theme in A Minor. It seemed scarcely possible for him to work harder, yet he did, to give the finishing touch to his program.

The hour arrived. Between two songs, while the singer rested, Ignace Paderewski began playing before Vienna's musicians and critics. They were not at first much interested in an unknown young Pole. But soon they began to be keenly interested. They had not expected to see anyone of this distinguished, even beautiful, appearance; more than that, here was a magnetic personality. In short, they were impressed first with his looks and the kind of person he seemed to be, then more and more with his playing, as Leschetizky had been certain they would be. After he finished there was excited applause. Nothing so stirred Austria's top artistic circle as the discovery of musical genius, and a performance that promised a golden career. While critics hurried home to write, others stayed to congratulate the pianist. The next morning the name Ignace Jan Paderewski was known to all the musical people of Vienna.

His first thanks went to the teacher who had made possible the forward step. Young as he was, Ignace Paderewski's head was not turned by this success. He was thinking of the work to be done before he could try again. He was thinking of Paris.

CHAPTER IV

"Lion of Paris"

FORTUNATELY the moving picture had not yet been invented. This country boy had grown into such a strikingly handsome young man that film producers would have pursued him. And he terribly needed now to concentrate on the piano, free from distracting offers.

It was not only his remarkable head that made people stop on the street to look at him—the burning blue eyes set far apart, the long, well-shaped nose and sensitive mouth, the crown of hair. There was something in the way he held himself, the way he walked, a kind of natural sureness and dignity that impressed them.

Nor did his clothes take away from the simplicity of his appearance, as often happens. He did not wear the high, stiff collar fashionable at that time. His full, strong throat needed to be free while he practiced; only in a low, soft collar and soft bow tie was he comfortable. When playing in public he felt best wearing a white shirt, this same loose tie, a white waistcoat with his dark suit.

During that first tour with his violinist friend, when they had set out on a quick road to fame, he had learned a great deal about audiences. "Is there anything they don't see or hear?" he exclaimed one day. Since then he had discovered

how much they expect, and have a right to expect. They
want to feel, above all, that an artist is being honest with
them, giving his best, and that he respects them enough to
look his best too. "Only a fool thinks lightly of his audience,"
he said.

Now he was to face an audience whose approval or disapproval counted more than that of any other in the world that
was to be his world: a French audience, used to hearing the
finest in music and in performance. Paris not long ago had
gone wild over the playing of Rubinstein and Liszt, the most
brilliant pianists of their time. If Paderewski let his mind
dwell on these things instead of fixing it on his fingers, he
might be beaten at the start.

A debut in Paris isn't lightly arranged. Leschetizky's wife,
Madame Essipoff, was there, as well as others whom Modjeska
had interested; she herself was playing in the United States.

"Without these wonderful friends," Ignace wrote his
father, "how could I have come? Those I told you about
who urged me at Strasbourg to go to Paris have invited me to
give a first private recital in their house here, where I will
meet many persons in the musical and social world. Then
Madame Essipoff has already arranged with the Erard piano
firm for my first public concert in their fine hall."

He reported to the Kerntopfs too the rapid progress of
events, and as soon as it was settled sent them the date of his
concert, March third.

"My friends beg me," he added, "not to worry; they feel
that I am well enough known to make it certain the hall will
be filled." It was unnecessary to tell his father or Edward
about the great number of Poles in France, for all Poles

had known of that for a hundred years; in fact, ever since the carving up of their country, Paris had been called Poland's capital. Thousands who refused to live under a conqueror called France their home. The Polish colony hummed with interest in this debut of a Polish youth said to have unusual talent.

Winter had not quite ended, spring not quite begun. There is always something magical in the air of Paris, in its glorious parks and along the Seine River. Paderewski, however, shut himself away from this. He concentrated all day on work with hands, fingers, memory, and once more reviewed each composition he was to play. He dared not let down one moment. Waves of nervousness, doubting questions tortured him. Am I too young? Trying too soon, when I've still so much to learn? Then belief in himself flooded back. It was March 3, 1889; it would soon be time to start for the Salle Erard. He dressed carefully, in white shirt and waistcoat, black coat and trousers, and brushed back his thick hair.

After he arrived at the hall he studied the stage, the piano, the chair, and the distance he must walk from his dressing room; he decided on each move he would make, leaving nothing to chance.

The manager was at his elbow. He was surprised when the young pianist said, "Please have half the gaslights turned out just before I begin to play."

"Is that wise?" the manager asked. "Some in the audience may not like it." But he hurried off to give the order.

Paderewski had learned that he felt blinded, found it almost impossible to play, when there was a glare on the keyboard. He looked again at stage, walls, distances, till the whole scene was clear in his mind. Then he went back to the dressing room and asked that no one for any reason be allowed to enter. He shut the door. Even his father, Antonina, Edward, had they been in Paris—and how he wished they were!— would not have been allowed to see him during this half-hour.

He bent all his will to fix his mind on his program. He would play first a rather severe, classical number—Beethoven's Thirty-two Variations in C Minor; then a Chopin group, which he would interpret in his own way, a new way. People were apt to think of Chopin as a composer of music that had only exquisite, dreaming beauty. He would stress Chopin's brilliance, his power. Last he would play Liszt's Rhapsody Number Six in D flat.

While he sat quietly in the small dressing room, his audience was pouring into the hall. The élite of the Polish and French aristocracy filled the first rows. Famous musicians, painters, sculptors, actors, and actresses crowded in, conspicuous among them the white-haired Gounod, loved for himself as well as for his opera *Faust*. Tchaikovsky, celebrated Russian composer, was there, and practically all the great musicians of the day except the Belgian, César Franck, who lived almost like a hermit. Massenet had come, as had the much-fought-over modern, d'Indy.

This was the time in France when Sarah Bernhardt, "the Divine Sarah," ruled the French stage; when Mistral was writing great poetry, Rodin carving immortal sculpture. Oh, Paris could gather wit and learning, talent and grace to make a hall shine! No one in the audience was more interested than were Colonne and Lamoureux, the two conductors of the two best French orchestras. Each had decided to engage this young Pole at once for a concert if he proved as good as people said he was.

Suddenly lights were turned low. There was a buzz; some objected. They craned their necks; they wanted to see this young man. He walked with an elastic step to the piano. They liked that. They liked the way he quietly took his place, with no pose, nothing theatrical about him. He began the Beethoven "Variations." As their eyes got used to the half-light the people could see his face now under the crown of bright hair. They began to feel the magnetism of this vivid personality, the beauty of what this poet at the piano felt and expressed, in these tones and rhythms. He seemed to be casting a spell upon the hall. A tide of responsive emotion swept across the tense rows. When the concert came to an end, with Liszt's "Rhapsody," the two conductors raced to the platform. Lamoureux won.

"I must have a concert," he said breathlessly, "and soon. People will be impatient. They will insist on hearing you again at once."

Paderewski hadn't time to think. Proud Poles, artists, others crowded around him, praising, congratulating, repeating, "More concerts, please, and don't make us wait!" These words rang louder in his ears than all the praise. "A concert soon!"

He had come to Paris with enough compositions studied and memorized for one concert, and that preparation had taken the greater part of a year. He had hoped only for a certain success, for enough money to return to Vienna, to go on with his studies with Leschetizky. Now Lamoureux spoke of a concert in three weeks. Paderewski was too tired to face what that meant.

I shouldn't have come till I had more pieces prepared, he thought miserably, for he realized that he couldn't go away if he wanted to keep what Paris had just given him. He would have to study and memorize a new program and play it in three weeks. If Paris thinks I'm better than I really am, I've got to *be* better than I am! These thoughts ran like lightning across his brain while he bowed and shook hands, smiled and thanked this company that seemed not to want to leave. Finally it was over. He had agreed to give the concert Lamoureux wanted.

He went home with friends for a late supper and a game of cards. He could have been very happy about this night were it not for that other night that loomed now only three weeks ahead. He was terribly tired; a quiet game would soothe nerves; cards and billiards always did that. In the morning he would begin work.

During the next three weeks he scarcely knew he was in Paris; he rarely took even a quick walk in one of its parks or along the river. Often he said desperately, "It's simply impossible. I can't build a program in time." Then he would let himself think what the news of his success would mean in Sudylkow and Warsaw, in Zakopane, when Modjeska was home again.

He was sending on an assortment of press clippings to Antonina, including an amusing one that pictured him as "The Lion of Paris." It was helpful to think of Leschetizky's satisfaction. Madame Essipoff had sent him a full report. Such thoughts revived him, especially on days when he practiced fourteen or seventeen hours. He was preparing, among other numbers, Saint-Saëns' Piano Concerto in C Minor and a Hungarian Fantasia by Liszt.

On March twenty-third he gave his second public concert. And the audience again went wild, the grand old composer Gounod leading the bravos! The more people saw of the young Pole, the more they valued him. Here was a person with not only a single gift, but with a brilliant all-around mind. The French like nothing better than a *bon mot*. At this time the composer Saint-Saëns gave them one that has lived to this day. After the concert he said, "Paderewski is a genius who happens also to play the piano."

Invitations came pouring in from other French cities. Paderewski made a rapid tour. He hurried to Belgium to play, and to Germany, where a Hamburg paper said, "His Chopin electrified his audience," where in Munich "The public acted as if crazy with joy."

If all this was desperately hard work, it was rewarded by one success after another and by enough money saved for a return to Vienna to prepare at least two more programs. But first Paris made him promise to come back. Nor was it hard to promise. Already he loved this sparkling city, where in certain quarters scarcely a girl or boy, man or woman on the street was without a painting or a music score carried under the arm, or an architect's drawing or a poem.

"Here, more than in any other place," he wrote, "an artist can find that stimulus he needs to create. When I come back I'll write a concerto here."

For, though Paderewski was fully embarked on his pianistic career, he had by no means given up his other work, that of composing. He felt that music played dies when the tone ceases; music written can last for centuries. Men in the eighteen-eighties did not foresee the phonograph record.

Along with other musicians, young and old, Paderewski was following a fierce battle of that decade over the question, "Shall we allow Wagner's music to be played?" Paris shook with it. The Franco-Prussian War was too recent. People looked at the black-draped statues in the Place de la Concorde, representing the beautiful French provinces of Alsace and Lorraine, seized by the victorious Germans, and said, "No, we can endure nothing German, not even great music."

When *Tannhäuser* was put on it was beaten down by howls and hisses. There were riots inside and outside the historic opera house. People on the streets were furious. *Lohengrin* started a similar uproar, but the opera management battled on and *Lohengrin* kept its place on programs. In the end Wagner's operas were performed, as Paderewski believed they should be. If riots over music seem strange to us now, we have to remember many such controversies during and after World War II even in the United States, remember that it was a long time before some people would listen to a German opera. We may believe that great art belongs to all people, but war fire blinds long after guns cease.

When Paderewski got back to Vienna, Leschetizky was away; however, he started in at once to work on new programs. After the master teacher's return, they had wonderful hours together.

"I have only praise for what you have accomplished," Leschetizky said. "I've no doubts about these programs. They are bound to please. With the old one, you now have three."

"If they please you, then I am *sure* of them." Voice and eyes spoke gratitude.

In the meantime, Vienna asked for a concert. This time Paderewski played without orchestra and was hailed as a bright new star in the sky. He laughed. "Something else to send Antonina."

If he had let "lions and stars" turn his head, his career might have ended then and there. But he looked forward, not backward. It is time to keep my promise, he thought. He got ready to return to Paris.

Probably no one in that city of excitement ever had two more exciting seasons than he now lived through. He saw his name in every paper, heard it on all the boulevards, saw caricatures of himself on walls, photographs in shop windows. People fought to entertain him after his concerts, offering another test of a young man's steadiness.

"I have enough money now to have my boy come on," he wrote Edward. But always behind the glittering success hung the shadow. His bright, eager boy still couldn't walk. This success meant something terribly real—new doctors, the best tutors, everything he could do for his son. Edward brought Alfred as far as Vienna, and another Paderewski friend came with him to Paris. Paderewski spent his heart on the child; they had wonderful times together. But so far, no doctor had done much for the boy; they said he would never be able to travel with his father. So it was arranged that Alfred should live as comfortably, as happily as possible in France with the violinist Gorski and his wife Helena, who now made Paris their home. There Paderewski could see him oftener.

At this time too he had another satisfaction—fortunately

one without a shadow. "What will I ever be able to do to repay all your kindness?" he had often asked Edward Kerntopf. Now he thought of something that would please him enormously. There was to be a World's Fair in Paris. He wrote Edward about it, adding, "You must exhibit your pianos at this Exposition. I will make all the arrangements; all you have to do is send them on." The Kerntopf pianos arrived and, to Paderewski's delight, won a gold medal.

Again, he had to move on. The road, so far, had led from Vienna to Paris, to Belgium, to Germany, then back to Vienna and Paris. Now it pointed to London. He had three programs at his fingertips, and a spectacular success to his credit. There was no stopping now. Modjeska had told him it would be so: in building a career one cannot stop; it is like building a beautiful tower, laying stone upon stone, so long as life lets one.

CHAPTER V

London and the Provinces

THE greater Paderewski's success became, the higher were his expenses. He now had a capable secretary to take charge of letters that piled up on his desk, and a valet to see that he had clean shirts ready and suits properly pressed for quick changes; his manager, or agent, usually demanded a large sum. Henceforth he must make more money.

Teachers often ask what thrusts a certain pupil forward. In the Warsaw Conservatory many bright girls and boys wanted more than anything else to be musicians, and dreamed of careers. They worked hard and played well, but were not destined to be known outside their homeland; while their mischievous classmate "Squirrel" would play across the world, be known to and loved by that world. Was this because he worked harder, longer, was born with a stronger body, better memory, quicker eyes and ears? Because he had a mind that reached out farther than theirs, was more conscious of all its surroundings, understood more about what the totality of life is? Or did a mysterious force called luck guide him?

Perhaps it was chiefly because of something different from all these things, something often called the "divine gift," which makes the poet dream dreams, and is given only to a few in any one generation—the gift that reveals and teaches. Is this divine fire inherited, from a gifted mother, father, or grandparent? It may be, scientists say, but sometimes a genius springs from apparently ungifted parents, from some unknown, wretched street of poverty.

But though people can't explain just what the gift is, they recognize it when it appears. Now they were saying a young Pole possessed it.

In terms of miles, London is not far from Paris. Paderewski took a train north to the French coast, thinking as he rode through the richly patterned farm region how much his father, Antonina, and his boy would like it. If I earn more, he thought, why not rent a farm and bring them all here for a vacation—Edward too? He crossed the choppy English channel and in about ten hours reached the largest city in the world, and added another river to his collection. For as Warsaw draws life from the Vistula, Vienna from the Danube, Paris from the Seine, so London draws it from the muddy, barge-crowded Thames. But though in miles not far, Paderewski saw at once that in its different ways of doing things Queen Victoria's capital was indeed a long way from Paris.

He had watched with a thrill of anticipation the three Erard pianos being packed in their huge cases, one for his hotel room, two for his concerts. He had boarded the train with greater confidence than he had ever before felt. He liked little Mr. Daniel Mayer, who was managing the English recitals and who met him at the station in London; he seemed honest, direct.

"My English isn't anything to boast of, but I'm working

on it," Paderewski apologized, as they entered the hotel room where the piano was already installed.

"Oh, don't worry about the language," Mayer laughed. "You'll pick it up fast, now that you'll be hearing it all the time. And you'll find that many people speak French."

Mayer left. Paderewski got ready to practice; for once he did not feel pressed. He had already played these programs for audiences that had overwhelmed him with bravos. Things could scarcely have looked more promising. His first concert was booked for Saint James's Hall on May ninth; this was the summer of 1890.

He was therefore completely unprepared for a cold, indifferent London, a London not pleased with the highly colored reviews in the French press, suspicious of his talent precisely because of the sensational reports. His manager, Mayer, used the name given by the French—"Lion of Paris" —on the posters advertising Paderewski's London performances. But the English weren't in the habit of rushing out to welcome Paris "lions"! Even the weather seemed hostile. On the day of the concert, winds tore the park flowers from their beds; rain drenched those Londoners who stayed on the streets.

"This weather couldn't be worse," Paderewski said gloomily to Mayer, who bustled in to report how things were going. He turned on another light. He was always extremely sensitive to his surroundings; he felt what was in the air. With every hour he grew more depressed. Mayer had to admit that tickets were not selling. Indeed, he made no progress in trying to cheer his pianist.

As the concert time neared Paderewski was in the grip of a dreadful nervousness. "I can't possibly play," he said wretchedly. "So much for fine confidence; this shows what it's worth!" Struggling against such a mood, he rode through wind and rain to Saint James's Hall.

The hall was not half filled! He walked to the piano he had so recently played on that marvelous night in Paris. The red-gold of his hair set off the pallor of his face. People saw that he was nervous. But the firmly set lips under the blond mustache he now wore told them he had himself in hand. He would do his best even in this disheartening place.

Finally a part of the small audience did applaud warmly. But after the swiftness and splendor of the successes across the channel, this English debut was nothing short of catastrophe, financially as well as musically. Mayer was stunned. Nor did he hope for much from the press. Yet he little suspected critics could be so ruthless.

The reviews ran the gamut between extreme disapproval and extreme approval, but there was far more fault-finding than praise. They called this young Pole's playing vulgar, violent, much noise and little music, charged him with striving to astonish. It seemed almost as if they had conspired together to pull Paderewski down from whatever height he might think he had won. Nor was the shock eased by the enthusiasm of the few critics who found a crystalline clarity, an overwhelming power combined with an exquisite delicacy of touch in his playing, who called his interpretation of Chopin compelling.

As he and his manager tried to account for this situation, Paderewski said, "Your billboard posters are at least partly to blame. If I had known I would never have allowed them. 'Lion of Paris'—as if a circus were arriving!"

"No, you're wrong; people like that kind of striking line." Mayer defended his poster but he never used it again.

Those who knew Paderewski saw how completely unjust was the charge that he sought sensational effects, and understood how it hurt him. He was simple and honest in private and in public. He never indulged in posturing at the piano; there was no swaying back and forth. When he had to return to the stage again and again before an audience that might be almost hysterical he preserved a quiet dignity. There was never a false note in either the way he looked or the way he acted.

Clearly there was nothing to do now but grit his teeth and live down this bad start if he could. "Do my best"—that was the phrase that rang in his brain.

Little by little London responded. More people heard the second recital than the first, more the third than the second. But he was so shaken by the strain of the unexpected experience that when Mayer ran in one day to tell him that the next, the last concert of the series, an all-Chopin recital, was sold out, he seemed scarcely to listen.

Then there was other trouble. Mayer was sending a pamphlet ahead to towns on the provincial tour he was about to begin. He combed newspaper columns for enough favorable sentences to give an attractive impression of the London concerts.

Paderewski read the flattering pamphlet and threw it on the table. "If there is to be any advertising," he declared grimly, "it will tell the whole truth. I will not allow you to select a few lines and send them out to give this false picture. If anything goes out, the worst goes too!" He was terribly in earnest. The silly "lion" poster was a small matter compared with this.

Mayer urged, argued. "Such a thing has never been done, *can't* be done. It will ruin you."

But Paderewski would not budge. An extraordinary new circular was printed and posted.

Oddly enough, for the provinces it proved to be about the best advertisement he could have had. For just as London wasn't keen about following Paris, many English towns liked to make their judgments independently of London. "London has pretty savagely criticized this young man's playing," people said. "We'll see what we think about it." They bought tickets. Audiences grew until halls were packed.

Paderewski returned to London, thin, tired, but with a very successful tour to his credit. We can chuckle over what followed—his amazing conquest of the London that had previously received him so coldly. For the fair-haired young Polish pianist became an even greater sensation in England than he had been in France. Days before a concert date, lines formed in front of Saint James's Hall—some people brought their breakfasts! And when he again played in the provinces, often every seat was sold two months in advance. The first London concert had netted about fifty dollars, these later ones about five thousand dollars each.

Box-office receipts as well as enthusiasm continued to mount. Women pulled flowers from their dresses to throw on the concert stage, crowds refused to leave until lights were actually turned off. Social leaders vied with one another to engage the pianist for private recitals. However, though these paid well, he disliked playing at receptions, with their thoughtless interruptions, late-comers, chatter, and scraping chairs. People were to learn that he respected his art too highly to tolerate disturbances. On one occasion he suddenly stopped playing. "I regret extremely," he said icily, "to interrupt such pleasant conversation. When it is finished, I will continue." However he did enjoy playing in certain houses where there was a true appreciation of music—a musical atmosphere.

Paderewski was always most sensitive to the quality of a voice; if hard or shrill, it actually hurt him. One reason why he particularly admired the American novelist Henry James, whom he met at this time in London, was his quiet, kindly voice. "The voice of a good man," he called it. Voice, to him, was a sure clue to character.

He was beginning to make such enduring friendships that until he came to the United States he called England his second home—strange climax to dreadful months! To his father and Antonina, in the Polish village, to the Kerntopfs and Warsaw friends, the mere outline of these later London experiences sounded like an *Arabian Nights* tale.

In English houses, talk usually turned to politics and government. On his many visits Paderewski met men who were to play leading roles in that terrible World War drama for which the stage was being set, though few saw it coming as he did. The English statesman he most admired and with whom he formed close ties of friendship happened to be the

one who could best help him, the greatly loved Lord Balfour, a wise, simple man, an altogether noble character.
They had many a talk about Poland's long martyrdom.

"But a century and a half of it has not broken our spirit,"
Paderewski would say. "My father would prove that to you."

Since he always tried to turn people's thoughts from himself to his country, he was deeply moved when the English
musician Sir Edward Elgar, in dedicating a composition to
him, called it "Polonia," because it was inspired by thoughts
of Poland.

These discussions of England's and Europe's problems, of
Poland's hope for freedom, often took place at supper parties
after a concert or after the opera or a play, when Paderewski
went home, as he often did, with Sir Henry Irving or another
great actor or singer. Alongside political exchanges ran those
about painting and the other arts. The battle over Wagner's
music raged hotly in London too. Now that a stirring fight
was on, people who previously had not particularly cared for
music wouldn't miss a Wagner opera; and, in order to take
part in the controversy, they began listening to and studying
other kinds of music, and thus increased Paderewski's own
box-office receipts.

In this world metropolis that loved discussion, there was
no more brilliant talk than that heard in the house of the
painter Sir Lawrence Alma-Tadema. Here Paderewski was
most at home, and would be whenever he returned to England. In the studio, he watched the progress of the painting
of many canvases that hang in London Galleries today, and of
his own portrait; for when Sir Lawrence asked him to pose
he gaily consented. Several persons lucky enough to have

been intimates in the Alma-Tadema household have described
the extraordinary scene in the studio while Paderewski's portrait was being painted. Sir Lawrence's wife and his daughter
Anna said they too would like to make sketches, and Queen
Victoria's daughter, Princess Louise, asked to join them. So,
when a beautifully wrought chair was placed in the middle
of the studio, and the pianist took his pose, four breathlessly
intense painters chose positions around him. He had not foreseen that necessary sittings would continue more than a week,
or counted the strain involved in his trying to help each
painter to get the view most desired.

To break the tension he chatted when he could with Sir
Lawrence's younger daughter, Laurence, who sat just out
of reach of the brushes, quietly sewing, and enjoying the
hectic scene. An onlooker, if asked to choose the person in
this group likely to become one of Paderewski's most helpful
friends, would scarcely have selected the girl Laurence; but
so it proved to be.

When a gong gave the signal for lunch, Paderewski leaped
from his chair. Both painter and pianist believed in the seriousness of work, but work was to be done, not talked about.
Neither of them talked shop at table. Instead they matched
amusing stories, laughing and joking throughout the meal;
then, after it, went back to the studio.

No one of the Alma Tadema studio portraits became so
popular as a small, silver-point drawing made about this time
by Sir Edward Burne-Jones, whose willowy knights and
angels are prominent in many English collections. Later the
original hung in the Paderewski house in Switzerland. People
have told various stories of how Burne-Jones came to make

this much-loved portrait sketch. The one most often quoted reports that one day, when the tall, dignified Pre-Raphaelite painter was walking along the street, he passed Paderewski and was so struck by his appearance, particularly by the glory of his hair, that he went back to pass him again, then rushed home to his studio where he exclaimed, "I've seen an archangel treading the London streets," and began drawing furiously, from memory, that beautiful head with its halo of red-gold hair. When, a few days later, a friend brought the unsuspecting Pole to the studio to call, Burne-Jones shouted, "You are my archangel!" and persuaded him to sit at once. In two hours he had completed the sketch that became famous the world over.

It would take a volume to describe in detail the highlights of these London experiences; Paderewski's first visit to Windsor Palace, to which he was invited by Queen Victoria, was one of the most memorable.

"One day in June, 1891, a letter on white note-paper surmounted by a crown and the words 'Windsor Castle' in blue print, signed by Sir Walter Parratt, the Queen's Master of Music, arrived. Paderewski was requested to play before Queen Victoria. The Queen-Empress no longer took part in the artistic or the social life of her people, but to play for her was a great honor. . . .

"Paderewski left London in the evening, going by train to Windsor. When he arrived at the Castle it was after nine o'clock and the Master of the Household was awaiting him. He was led through half-lit passages and high rooms to a large drawing room with green paneled walls, containing occasional tables bearing many photographs and souvenirs. A piano stood in a corner of the room, near a window. At nine-forty-five, five minutes before the appointed time, a door was opened and the Queen walked in, leaning heavily on a stick. She looked exactly as Paderewski had pictured her; clad in black, short, stout, with heavy eyelids. But her shortness had a grandeur in keeping with a much taller person. The simplicity of her dress strengthened this picture of a Queen who was half legend, half symbol. . . .

"The Queen was accompanied only by her youngest daughter, Princess Beatrice, and one or two ladies and gentlemen in attendance. She nodded appreciatively or applauded after each piece, and when the program was finished she asked Paderewski to go on. Yes, some more Chopin, and some Schumann too, but above all some Mendelssohn, please, some of his old songs. When Paderewski had finished playing Mendelssohn, the Queen thanked him in a voice in which even royal self-discipline could not master entirely the undertone of emotion. And she began to tell Paderewski about the days when Mendelssohn used to come to the Castle to give her music lessons, and about the nervousness, nay, the fright, she always felt before a lesson. Later in the evening, when the Queen retired to her rooms, she opened her diary and wrote: '2 July, Windsor Castle. Went to the green drawing room and heard Monsieur Paderewski play on the piano. He does so quite marvelously, such power and such tender feeling. I really think he is quite equal to Rubinstein. He is young, about 28, very pale, with a sort of aureole of red hair standing out.' "[1]

[1] *Ignace Paderewski, Musician and Statesman*, by Rom Landau. New York: Thomas Y. Crowell Company, 1934.

But, however real the thrill of great occasions, Paderewski often said, "I get my deepest pleasure from playing quietly for a friend or two." Success piled on success did not take away his need of simple, direct relationships. The natural sincerity of this fun-loving, warmhearted country boy, always looking for noble qualities in others and finding them, remained unchanged as he grew older. That is what Americans at once felt about him when he arrived in New York.

CHAPTER VI

New York

STEINWAY AND SONS, New York piano makers, had established a concert bureau, not with an eye to box-office receipts, but to win fame for their instruments. They booked outstanding American and foreign artists for programs played on Steinway pianos. After the newspapers reported Paderewski's Paris and London triumphs, the Steinway firm invited him to give a series of concerts, offering thirty thousand dollars for eighty performances.

New York, that fabulous United States Modjeska had pictured! Without realizing, any more than the Steinways did at the time, how unfair the offer was, Paderewski accepted it.

On November 3, 1891, wearing a fur-collared overcoat and a small bowler hat topping the famous mass of red-gold hair, he boarded a small ship. This was his first ocean voyage; it remained one of his memory's nightmares. After days of gales and mountainous seas, he looked so ill that his worried secretary tried to revive him by picturing the thrill of arrival and welcome.

As the battered boat nosed its way across a murky bay toward a dingy dock, Paderewski, peering through the drizzle, saw nothing to thrill him. On the wet pier the Steinway agent's gloomy welcome—"I must warn you, Mr. Paderewski, not

to expect here the successes you have had in Europe"—
seemed but a part of the whole dismal prospect.

When the pianist looked about the hotel where the agent
had engaged rooms for him and his secretary, he was stunned.
Never in Poland or elsewhere in Europe had he been housed
in a place so run down, so dirty. Yet he tried to settle down
for the night; he was to make his first rehearsal appearance at
Carnegie Hall with Walter Damrosch's orchestra the following morning. Sleep? The bed seemed to heave with bugs.
Mice ran wildly up and down behind the wainscoting. Every
noise from below broke through the flimsy door. What to
do? he asked himself desperately. Send his secretary out in
the night rain of this strange city to find another hotel? No,
he decided he must wait for morning. The next day part of
the time so needed for practice was given to moving.

How he managed to play that night as well as he did the
Saint-Saëns Concerto in C Minor and his own A Minor Concerto, he could not have explained. He did know that one
thing that had helped him was the fact that he at once liked
the young orchestra conductor, Walter Damrosch.

The gross returns from the concert were only five hundred
dollars. Some in that first New York audience were extremely enthusiastic, others less so. The same was true of
critics. However, the most eminent New York music critic
at this time, Henry T. Finck, listened with such imaginative
perception and set down such exact comment on Paderewski's playing, particularly of his use of the pedal—a rapid
successive use by which he gave the piano new power to
change the quality of the tone after it had been struck—that
today people not fortunate enough to have heard him turn

back to Finck's pages to learn how Paderewski played. They turn also to those of another outstanding New York critic of that time, James Huneker. Huneker stressed the splendor, the nobility of Paderewski's style, his brilliancy and endurance, his luscious touch, the dreamy poetry of his interpretations. Later, when he looked for an explanation of the immense enthusiasm of this Pole's audiences, the crowded halls from New Orleans to Seattle, he found the answer in these great qualities which he had discovered in Paderewski's first Carnegie Hall concert. These qualities, Huneker said, gave the pianist the power of rousing an audience from a state of calm indifference to wildest frenzy. He asked unbelievers to go and with their own ears and eyes hear and witness what he had heard and witnessed.

An artist could scarcely hope for more able, more deeply felt appraisal than those of Finck and Huneker. Yet, on the whole, Paderewski's first appearance in the United States could not be called a success. But neither was it a failure. It was, to the Pole, a challenge.

After the concert he hurried back to his new hotel, the Windsor, on Fifth Avenue about four blocks south of Saint Patrick's Cathedral, to begin practicing the two concertos he was to play the next time. The rehearsal of the second concert was set for ten o'clock the following morning in Carnegie Hall. The Steinway firm had arranged that he should play no less than six great piano concertos during his first week in the United States and give no less than six recitals in the two following weeks! Where could he find time to prepare such a fantastic program, to say nothing of time to rest!

The dates were fixed, the concerts advertised. He would

have to do his best in these appalling circumstances. Now to his piano, to concentrate.

There was a knock on the door. Paderewski opened it and admitted the embarrassed hotel manager. It wasn't easy for him to say to this courteous, tired young foreigner, who must be having a hard enough time at best to get started in a strange country, "I'm sorry, Mr. Paderewski, but you won't be able to practice in your room. It's not allowed in the hotel." Rehearsal was set for ten in the morning! Almost ill, dreadfully in need of sleep, Paderewski dropped into a chair. The contrast between what he had been told about the United States and what confronted him was so staggering that he asked himself bitterly, almost hopelessly, why he had come.

Then suddenly a picture flashed into his mind. He saw himself in the Kerntopf warehouse, from a field of pianos choosing one. "Get your coat," he called to his secretary. "We're going to the Steinway warehouse!"

Into the night they went, down Fifth Avenue. At Fourteenth Street a shivering watchman opened the warehouse door. He lighted a pair of candles and set them on the piano Paderewski chose. There in the bitter cold the pianist practiced till dawn. At ten o'clock he met Walter Damrosch, ready for rehearsal; afterwards, he returned to the warehouse, practiced the rest of the day, and that night made his second, more successful appearance at Carnegie Hall.

He repeated the effort, practicing seventeen hours of the next twenty-four; and at the third of that first week's concerts he played a Rubinstein concerto and a Chopin concerto so brilliantly that he swept the audience that packed the hall right off its feet. Men rushed to the platform, wouldn't let

him go, had to be practically forced to leave the hall. Perhaps
he was beginning to find Modjeska's America!

However, there was still little time to think of anything
but practice. In only two days the series of six recitals would
start. The first week he had played with an orchestra. The
recitals he would play alone, although in New York it was
then customary for a pianist to share his recital with a singer
or violinist, to make sure the audience would not be bored.

He had chosen his programs—Beethoven, Schumann, Schubert, a Chopin group—as always—a composition of his own,
and a Liszt number. He counted on a good house.

"But," his secretary reported, "the Steinways have put the
recitals in the small Madison Square Garden Hall." This was
the last straw, after he had at such cost won his large audience.

"It's impossible!" he stormed as he walked rapidly up and
down the room. "Stupid! Unfair!"

"Most stupid. But it's too late to change."

"Too late for the first concert or two." He stopped walking. "But the series will finish in Carnegie Hall!"

As it did. Box-office receipts were as much as three thousand dollars for one concert; he was to receive thirty thousand
dollars for the series of eighty!

Never before in New York had such throngs demanded
seats for a pianist's recital. When the six concerts were finished, Paderewski felt solid American ground under his feet.
Most artists who have been successful in other countries have
had as a goal a tour in the United States. They have come,
won acclaim, made friends. But who became so quickly, so
happily, so actively a part of the American public as did
Paderewski?

And now Henry Finck, whose book, *Success in Music*, was about to be published, asked Paderewski to prepare a paper on *tempo rubato* (stolen time) for inclusion in this volume. Fortunately Paderewski was able to do so. His analysis of the proper and improper uses of *tempo rubato*—particularly of his own use of it—has been more illuminating to serious students of music than almost any comment by others on this technique, and it reveals the secret of his interpretive genius.

Paderewski gave much time and thought to this paper. Up to that time little had been written about *tempo rubato*, which he called the foe of the metronome, and one of music's oldest friends—older than Mozart, older than Bach.

On the technical side, Paderewski said, *tempo rubato* consists of a more or less important slackening or quickening of the time or rate of movement. It is a fleeing away from the strict value of notes. Every interpreter should be able to use it judiciously, since it emphasizes the expression, introduces variety, infuses life into mechanical expression. It has always been used in the interpretation of national music, and frequently in popular music, especially dance forms. It is the use of *tempo rubato* that makes the Hungarian dances so fantastic.

It would be unthinkable, Paderewski maintained, to play Chopin without using *tempo rubato*. For, just as the heartbeat is changed by changing emotion, so musical rhythm is most delicately sensitive. Rhythm is order; but this order in music cannot proceed with the regularity of a clock. In the course of the dramatic development of a musical composition the initial themes change their character; consequently the rhythm changes also, in conformity with that character; it has to be energetic or languishing, crisp or elastic, steady or capricious. Rhythm is life.

A composer's imagination and an interpreter's emotion are not bound to be humble slaves of either metronome or tempo. Every composer, when using words as *expressivo, con passione, teneramente*, demands a certain amount of emotion, and emotion excludes regularity. *Tempo rubato* then becomes an indispensable assistant, but with it unfortunately appears also the danger of exaggeration, which the interpreter must guard against. Excess of freedom is often more pernicious than the severity of the law.

Paderewski's playing of Chopin and Schumann showed most strikingly what this rhythmic freedom accomplished. But unless one had the music score in his hands and read its directions while listening, he couldn't tell just when the pianist was "stealing time" to put new beauty into a certain passage.

The late Olin Downes, music critic for the *New York Times* for a quarter of a century, and an ardent admirer of Paderewski, added a flashing metaphor to this discussion of the interpretation of music. "No composer," Downes wrote, "can fully indicate his ideas on music paper. The most careful directions he can put on score paper are only sign-posts of the most general kind. It is for the interpreter of intuitive insight, sympathy, and evocative power to bridge the gap that lies between the printed score paper and actual music when it is sounded. Across that gap, like an electric spark, must leap the responsive and creative spirit of the performer. A composition is seldom or never performed exactly as the composer conceived it."

Very early Paderewski had been called a "poet of the piano," one who used tones as a poet uses words. A poet is a singer, people said; this gifted young Pole makes the piano sing. He moves and lifts the hearts of men as a great poet does. Some of his first compositions were songs; he set to music many poems of Polish poets, of Mickiewicz, Slowacki, and others whose pages he so readily learned by heart when a boy. While he was still in Warsaw, one of his earliest critics called him a poet of overflowing fancy.

But no matter how completely he seemed lost in his playing, with him nothing "just happened." The slightest effect was the result of study, day after day, month after month. "I often practice a piece that I know by heart," he told a beginner once, "as if I had never heard it before." To play one crystal-clear passage the way he played it meant that he had to keep his body as fit as an athlete's; that he couldn't once neglect exercises of arms, hands, and fingers with apparatus he himself invented, or the careful massage, the final soaking of his hands in warm water, and limbering finger practice before a concert.

With this first New World battle fought and won, Paderewski tried to snatch a little rest. Here, as in every country, friends were quickly discovering his pleasure in games. "Paderewski could easily become the world's champion billiard player," Leschetizky once laughingly declared. A good game was a real vacation. Although Paderewski liked many people, he always found, wherever he went, one family with whom he felt especially at home: in Warsaw, the Kerntopfs; in Berlin, the Strausses; in London, the Alma-Tademas. He was most happy where there was a troop of romping children, even though he could scarcely endure thinking of Alfred, who could not romp.

In New York, too, he found such a family. Down on Eighth Street stood a modest house, a gathering place for writers, artists, great spirits of every kind. There the hospitable Gilders lived—the poet, Richard Watson Gilder, editor of the *Century Magazine*, his vivacious wife, and five children looking for fun. The early-American chairs and sofas that comfortably furnished the drawing room were not the kind children couldn't use. From his very first visit he loved that room. When he did not find Mark Twain there, ready for a talk and a laugh, or Kipling or Saint-Gaudens, Henry James or the marvelous Italian actress Eleonora Duse, there was certain to be some other inspiring person, and, best of all, the Gilders themselves.

If Mrs. Gilder happened not to be downstairs when Paderewski called, she was likely to discover him in the midst of a hilarious game with George and Rosamond and Francesca. One day George handed him his new knife to look at.

"A fine one. Are you giving it to me?"

Poor George had no such intention, yet how could he say so? After a difficult moment he pulled himself together. "I only got it yesterday!"

"A very good diplomat," Paderewski laughed, as he handed back the knife.

On another day he escorted Francesca, who had dark curls and dark eyes, to the piano.

"Now we will play a dance," he said, and his head with its

red-gold mop bent over hers with its tangle of dark curls. He guided her finger through the treble while he played ever so lightly the bass of his minuet.

The mood shifted, Francesca pulled the bright hair down over his eyes, clapped a cap on his head, and the two artists were off on a romp!

At this time Mr. Gilder was greatly interested in the building of the Washington Centennial Arch which stands today in Washington Square, New York; and Paderewski gave a benefit concert for the arch fund, which brought in forty-five hundred dollars.

In a letter thanking him, Mr. Gilder wrote that he and two others had climbed up three ladders and laid the last three stones of the structure. They carved their initials on hidden parts of these stones, and a large "P" for Paderewski took its place with the rest. "So your initial," Gilder said, "is built into the very structure of the monument and as long as the arch is remembered, your generous deed will be kept in mind."[1]

A little later, Mrs. Gilder wrote to a friend, "Paderewski has returned to his own, to the children who dote on him more than ever." True indeed! Did he ever "let on" if from the midst of a grand company he spied them huddling fearfully, deliciously, beneath the piano, separated only by glass doors from a small adjoining room from which they could reach a back stairway? Besides, screens obligingly placed helped them to creep unseen to their good listening post, a bit too good

[1] Adapted from *Letters of Richard Watson Gilder*, edited by his daughter Rosamond Gilder. New York: Houghton Mifflin Company, 1916.

during music, when thundering chords crashed down on their heads! No, he never let on.

"But," Mrs. Gilder adds, "he has been ill and suffered a great deal."

How could he escape paying for the strains of this tour? Besides the unavoidable stresses, there were avoidable ones; he remedied those as swiftly as possible—a wrong piano action, a chair too high, too low. When he found in Paris the "perfect chair" he had ordered it copied; from that day on, one of these low chairs with a padded, fringed seat traveled with him. Legs and back were detachable so that it could easily be packed into its special case. The public was quick to transfer a bit of ever-growing affection for their idol to this traveling chair. In a cartoon carried by newspapers across the country it was shown being taken from the case, marked "I.J.P." and covered with world labels.

When aching muscles proved that the action of a Steinway piano was too hard for him, he persuaded the makers to change it. But once they forgot to do this, and during a concert in upper New York State he suddenly felt a flash of excruciating pain; the tendons of his right arm were torn; the fourth finger refused to move. His face went gray, but he remained on the platform, forced the injured arm to go on with a Beethoven Sonata and the rest of the program.

From the hall he rushed to a doctor, who said, "Serious. All I can prescribe is a long, complete rest."

Other doctors gave the same opinion. In great pain, unable to practice, he thought desperately that his career might be already ended. Then battling determination went into action. He tried electricity, massage, treatments of all kinds, even some he invented himself. He managed to play the eighty concerts his contract required, and twenty-seven others which the Steinways arranged in order to make up for the unfair distribution of the profits from the first eighty. Paderewski received the entire sum netted by the extra recitals.

As if torn tendons were not enough, one of his fingers became badly infected. The doctor who operated on it also said, "This is serious. You must give your hand a complete rest. A week or two is not enough." But Paderewski had promised his friends Timothy and Joseph Adambowski of Boston, who were giving a concert on the very day of his operation, to play for them, and no one could prevent him from keeping that promise. There was blood on the keys when he finished, as there was after concerts that followed.

But as this first American tour finally neared its end, after he had gone from city to city, doctor to doctor, as far west as Chicago, his spirits rose. He felt sure that in Europe he would find the right treatment for his arm. So confident was he that he promised to return the following September; however, later, because of the arm, he changed September to December. Altogether he played one hundred and seven times in America, eighteen times in New York.

He had made enough money to rent a pleasant place in northern France where he could rest for a few months and have with him Alfred, his family, and old friends. His father was too ill to come, but Antonina came all the way from the Polish borderland, and Edward Kerntopf from Warsaw. Others came and went; the garden saw the gayest reunions.

Alfred loved it all. "I'm so happy," he would cry as his wheel chair sped by or as he listened, enchanted, hour by hour to his father's stories, or to Antonina's. If he saw them coming together, he got ready to laugh; he adored their jokes.

While Paderewski gave his arm rest, he again composed. It was during that summer of 1893 that he wrote his Polish Fantasia. After talking things over with Antonina and Edward he decided not to play at all the next season, 1893–94, but to find some quiet place where, while continuing to try to cure his arm, he would begin *Manru*, the opera that he had long wanted to write.

After that reunion he went first to Italy, but, because Alfred was not so well, returned to Paris. He hid in a small house near the city and worked all day on *Manru*, a story of gypsies, laid in the Tatra Mountain country near Modjeska's home. At night he enjoyed a good dinner in a restaurant where the coachmen of the quarter ate.

Months and money disappeared quickly. Alfred needed increasing care. News of Jan Paderewski's death brought profound grief. Yet Paderewski was thankful that his father had lived long enough to be happy about the success of his son, of which he had always been so certain.

CHAPTER VII

Across the United States

"DURING those first American tours, which cities seemed most interested in your music?"

"I will tell you about Kansas City." There was a twinkle in the blue eyes, no direct answer that could get him into trouble.

"As I saw it on my second tour, that part of Kansas City between hotels and the concert hall might have been a music quarter of Vienna, everywhere groups of enthusiasts, scores in hand, discussing programs. The air was filled with the music of talk about music. A large company traveled all the way from Texas, others from nearer points, to hear the two concerts, all students, lovers of music. It was a delight to play for them."

On the third tour, 1895–96, when Paderewski crossed the width of the continent to California, there were similar midwestern and far-western experiences. Trains brought teachers, students, and musicians, from outlying towns and farms to the concert city, often through snowdrifts, for winter is the music season. When word came that a train was held up, Paderewski waited for it if he could, as he did when he delayed his concert for a blizzard-caught Montana train bound for a Salt Lake City recital.

Occasionally his own train was late and thousands stayed on, once in a barn-like midwestern building on a below-zero night, hour after hour, refusing to leave. At intervals a town wit appeared on the platform to read fictitious telegrams, identical except for the name of the sending point: COMING ALONG JUST BROKEN THROUGH DRIFT AT X HOPE REACH HALL IN ONE HOUR. PADEREWSKI. When at midnight Paderewski arrived, worn out by the storm and worry over the delay, applause shook the walls. He hurried to the piano and played until three in the morning.

Always on these tours he made friends. Once a young woman reporter was sent from San Francisco to meet his private car on the Oakland side of the bay, to get an advance interview.

"But Mr. Paderewski is practicing. No one can see him now," the manager told her.

"I will wait." She settled down on the car step with a book, but she soon closed it and listened, fascinated, to a run, a chord, worked with, teased toward perfection, repeated, repeated until she lost count of the number of times. So, endless, patient work is the base of a golden success, she thought.

After an hour the manager returned. "Mr. Paderewski is free now and will see you."

She climbed the steps. He welcomed her with outstretched hand and a friendly smile. "But I'm afraid you have had to wait much too long." The interview got quickly under way. When it was time to go, Paderewski said, "But why not stay? We can cross the bay together and you can point out the sights."

A very young reporter on her first important assignment,

she could scarcely credit her luck. On the San Francisco side they parted friends.

When he came to play again she was sent a second time to report his arrival; they parted still better friends. Then there was a gap of several years; she married and no longer worked on the newspaper. With each year his fame had grown. When he returned she hesitated to call at the Palace Hotel. Late one afternoon her maid came upstairs and said, "There's a foreign gentleman to see you." She quickly went down. "You have not come to see me, so I have come to see you," he said.

Years later he rearranged a concert schedule in order to be present at her daughter's wedding; he had already sent as a wedding present to this daughter a gold mesh coin bag set with sapphires. Los Angeles expected him to play on the day of the wedding.

"Impossible," he said. "I must be in San Francisco. I suggest that you change your concert date."

"But why not change San Francisco's date?"

"I'm going to San Francisco for love."

The Los Angeles date was changed.

Experiences with weather explain why three pianos were used on Paderewski's tours. As soon as he arrived in New York he went to Steinway headquarters, where, from seven instruments ready for him to try out, he chose three whose tone and action he liked best. These were sent by express to cities where he was booked to play, in time to reach the hall at least ten hours before the concert, not only to cover possible delays, but also because the temperature of baggage car and concert hall so affects a piano's action that there must be time for it to get "accustomed" to the climate. Paderewski learned to take precautions; he carried with him a collapsible platform that could be fitted under piano and chair in six different ways to level up a sloping floor.

But on the whole he had to take things as they came. One night during a concert in a California seacoast town, boys were playing on the roof of the hall with parts of iron girders left there by workmen. Suddenly a horrified audience saw one of these parts hurtle down, almost striking the keyboard. Paderewski did not move but, as if unaware of his narrow escape, went on playing.

The third tour was a stupendous success. Before it was finished, crowds at stations asked, "When will you return? Next winter? We want to engage seats now." There was scarcely a town that did not display his photograph or a copy of the Burne-Jones drawing in at least one shop window. Everywhere audiences had begun to feel the very personal affection that grew with each of his tours, that made him, in turn, say of the United States, "It is my second home"—which later it actually became, when he bought a fruit ranch in California.

Ever since men have thought about what genius is they have asked how much it depends on character. The Chinese have an old saying which expresses what their profound philosophers thought: "Character is rarer than genius." And, in Europe, just before Paderewski's own time, the German poet Goethe said, "Character and personality are as important as genius." A president of the Royal Society of Great Britain, talking to the American National Academy about scientists and their discoveries, said, in a different way, the same thing: "More important than the fact the scientist discovers is the kind of man he is, the spirit in which he works, the spirit of good will, of love for all mankind." These sayings explain why people felt as they did, most without knowing why, about Paderewski.

He could not have endured the terrific fatigue of travel over this vast country, of continuous playing, with the waiting afterward to give encore upon encore to audiences he loved, if he had also had to face the hazards of unknown hotels, doubtful food, finding places to practice, loss of time in making train connections. Therefore he arranged, at great cost, to have a private car outfitted not only to travel in but to live in. The car was kept on side tracks in railway yards during stops. It had sleeping quarters for his staff, a tiny kitchen, and a homelike living room with attractive hangings, comfortable chairs, a piano, games, and books, chiefly biographies (among Americans, he particularly admired Benjamin Franklin). This little hotel on wheels was in the charge of a specially selected Pullman cook and crew; had its own lighting and heating system; and was connected with concert towns by telephone. The arrangement provided a pleasant home and also took care of the necessary routine.

When not playing, Paderewski usually rang for his morning tea late, then gave an hour to gymnastics, followed by three or four of practice at the piano. On concert days he retired to his bedroom about five in the afternoon, then, dressed for the performance and rejoined the others. After the concert lucky friends gathered in the car for dinner and a game of cards. He liked not to hurry that good dinner; after a day

of light eating and heavy work he was ready at eleven o'clock
for more than a tidbit. "*À table!*" he would call gaily when
the repast was ready. "We have an excellent fish tonight,"
or, "We have peaches," or "A fine cheese."

He had learned that no sleep was possible for the player
for hours after the intense emotional strain of playing a concert program, and dear to him were friends who could stay
with him to play bridge till three or four o'clock in the morning. After that he would sleep, amidst all the banging and
shrieking in the railway yard. There were strange scenes in
that grimy, bleak yard, as a dreamlike passage from Beethoven's "Moonlight Sonata," or crashing chords of a Liszt
Rhapsody, floated across it, and yardmen stopped to listen.
He liked to know they were there.

But the car drew other groups not so easily satisfied. Word
spread that Paderewski had instructed his cook to share
what he had with hungry men who asked for food. The steps
of the car were besieged, until finally the frantic chef took
matters into his own hands.

"No food to be had here," he shouted, brandishing any
kitchen weapon he could snatch. In time the crowd learned
that he meant it.

And Paderewski had to admit that it was impossible to cook
for all who wanted food. "However, you could give each
hungry person a half-dollar," he persisted. The master of the
kitchen knew what this would bring upon them, but he
obeyed, and then was forced, as he had foreseen, to put an
end to all gifts.

It was during his third American tour that Paderewski first
met a Stanford University engineering student whom he was

to meet again at an hour which neither of them could then have imagined. Many students were working their way through this new university, among them Herbert Hoover. When Hoover and a collegemate heard of the sensational success of Paderewski's San Francisco concerts, they made a daring plan, one that might earn them enough money to finance the rest of their college careers. They were then about the same age as Paderewski and the violinist had been when they set out from Warsaw on the unlucky tour that was intended to earn their conservatory expenses.

The plan was this: the two students would persuade the pianist to come from San Francisco to play in San Jose, a city in the flourishing fruit valley south of the university. Even without funds to start with, they could count on a hall and advertising for the famous Paderewski. They would guarantee twelve hundred dollars for the concert. This was a brilliant idea, one which might easily have put them a long way ahead. But they forgot, if, indeed, they ever knew, that in Holy Week many people will not attend even a concert.

Partly because their date fell in Holy Week, there was scarcely half an audience. They were stunned. They went to Paderewski's manager. "Mr. Paderewski will get what is due him," Herbert Hoover said. "The hall and the advertisers will have to accept our promise to pay. We will earn the money."

They went out to make arrangements. While they were out a message came. Mr. Paderewski wished to see them. "I have heard what you are doing," he said. "I think I have a better plan. You will first pay what you owe in this city. Then you will take thirty per cent of what remains for yourselves;

that is the customary manager's fee. What is left will be for me. I've enjoyed giving this concert for you."

"We do not want you to do this, Mr. Paderewski," Herbert Hoover objected. "We can—" But he got no further.

"No, I assure you, mine is the better plan. You must follow it."

"He's a prince," the younger student exclaimed. Herbert Hoover was silent as they hurried off to pay their bills.

CHAPTER VIII

More Travels
and Two Anniversaries

OF ALL his concerts during the last years of the nineteenth century and the beginning of the twentieth, none gave Paderewski more satisfaction than the ones he played in Warsaw, en route to Russia. His return was a great event for the conservatory; students and faculty crowded to hear him. Many of his schoolmates were there, and, of course, the Kerntopfs.

"I always knew," Edward cried, throwing his arm about his friend. "I always knew!" His teachers had their laugh when Edward taunted them with their dismal prophecies. "Well, have you changed your tune?"

Poles love to tease and laugh, to eat well and talk long. There was no lack of any of these lively activities during Paderewski's stay. Those classmates who had never traveled beyond half a dozen small towns were dazzled by his world-girdling adventures.

"To us anchored here," one of them said laughingly, "you're a comet blazing across the sky. Tell us, which country do you like best? After Russia, where next?" They plied him with questions at banquets and receptions; and at concerts they begged to hear his own compositions.

Late at night he and the Kerntopfs went home together, to recall until dawn the ups and downs of his student days, their relief and his father's joy when he finally won his diploma! He told them about Riond Bosson, a beautiful property he had bought in Switzerland—at last a home, where Alfred could run his wheel chair along garden and orchard paths. Alfred was making brilliant progress in his studies, had been writing amusing scripts for impromptu theatricals—favorite entertainment at the many parties in the comfortable house that was always overflowing with visitors.

Then Paderewski took the train for Saint Petersburg, this time wearing an overcoat with a warm fur lining. As he neared that gray city he thought, Well, I was able to pay Father back, with interest, those two hundred rubles. No one in the fashionable Russian audience that greeted him at the first of his four concerts remembered a penniless youth tramping their frozen streets. No one saw behind him, as he walked lightly across the stage to the piano, a plumber sharing bread and tea with him in a miserable underground room.

He met Russia's musicians and writers, whose prodigal gifts and tremendous energy he admired and envied, just as others admired and envied his. But interested as he was in Russian music and literature, he couldn't feel comfortable in that country. Any loyal Pole was bound to have unpleasant experiences there, and one as prominent as he would have more than others. He was glad to return to Warsaw.

He was impatient to return for another reason. His son Alfred had lived for many years with Madame Helena Gorska and his friendship for her and gratitude for the mother's devotion she gave Alfred had blossomed into the great love of his life. Modjeska often spoke of Helena as one of the most beautiful women she had ever seen, "with delicate features and large, wistful eyes." She was lively, sensitive; there was a complete harmony between her nature and Paderewski's. They were married in Saint John's Cathedral in Warsaw in May 1899, and then joined Alfred at Riond Bosson.

Shortly afterward, Paderewski's opera *Manru*, finished at last, was performed for the first time, in Dresden before an audience gathered from far and near. Leschetizky came from Vienna for the occasion. This opera, with its story of a gypsy lover, its colorful, romantic-tragic music, had a most promising start, though it is now rarely performed. The Metropolitan Opera in New York presented it the following year, on the same day that the composer was giving a recital in Carnegie Hall. Hundreds were turned away from both places; excitement in the music world reached a new high. Nothing like this had happened before. News writers watching for a striking headline were delighted. New Yorkers read, "Paderewski his own rival! Doubles his receipts to more than $20,000 in one afternoon!"

The opera finished, he began working on a third set of variations. "My best work for the piano," he called them. Besides, he was sketching his symphony.

He was playing in Spain, and feeling particularly hopeful about Alfred, who was to try a new treatment, when a telegram came. Alfred, not yet of age, had died suddenly of pneumonia. Overcome, Paderewski hurriedly canceled concerts. In Montmorency Cemetery, near Paris, where Chopin is buried, he and his wife buried his son of eager mind and hurt body.

The long double struggle to save his boy and to build a career had taken its toll; he felt broken, depressed. Soon, fortunately, he had to fix his thoughts on another concert tour, this time to the faraway, little-known continent, Australia, and neighboring New Zealand and Tasmania. Madame Helena had often hoped that she would one day see their strange birds and great fern-tree forests, and their boiling geysers. Accompanied by a doctor, they sailed with pianos and stools, trunks and bags, across the Red Sea and the Indian Ocean, and after more than a month on steaming waters they reached Melbourne in July; the city, they reported to Antonina, was colder than any other place in the world.

This trip included some of Paderewski's most dangerous adventures. At times the carriage jolted ahead over narrowest roads that edged dizzying precipices; but, though the rough progress over such stretches was particularly painful because of his neuritis, he was inspired by what he saw. He always felt an explorer's joy in the discovery of new forms in nature.

To his wife it was a most amusing trip. "My head is a spinning top," she said, as she followed bright-plumaged, chattering birds through the forests and secured specimens to take home with her. At the end of the tour they were traveling with a flock of forty or fifty birds in various-sized cages. The sight of them threw porters into a dither.

The collection started with Cocky Roberts, a superb green parrot with a white crown and dark tail feathers. For when he was brought in to brighten a rainy day he began joking, swearing, and commenting with such uncanny cleverness that the Paderewskis were enchanted. Cocky Roberts later traveled with them to New York. At Riond Bosson, where he ruled the house, he insisted on staying in the room while his master practiced. He would perch on the pianist's foot, undisturbed by the pedaling, apparently listening to each note, and at the end of a piece he would cry, "Oh Lord, how beautiful!"

Paderewski's strenuous world treks had pushed him to the brink of a nervous breakdown. To get rest, away from the piano, he bought a farm in Switzerland, not far from Riond Bosson, and spent part of his time for several years in developing peach, pear, apple, and cherry orchards and in breeding fine pigs and cows. He often fled to this retreat, where, free from intrusion, he worked with trees and animals, while his wife cooked and "kept camp." But though it paid good dividends in health, the farm, like other farms he bought or leased—indeed, like all his business investments—proved financially disastrous. Either in this way, or in gifts to patriotic projects or to the needy in Poland and in other countries, most of the huge sums he made disappeared.

The three neighbors who determined to erase the map of Poland from all geographies, and the very memory of Poland from men's minds, seemed to have succeeded. But Paderewski was daily proclaiming their certain defeat. It would be interesting to see a world map which marked the hospital doors, the doors of obscure rooms or apartments at which the musician suddenly appeared, asking if Poles were suffering there, and how he could help. In whatever city he found himself he searched the newspapers for items about his countrymen and, if he could, visited those in trouble. But no map shows Paderewski moving quietly on his mission of love, to rekindle his people's faith.

As the rule of the three powers stretched on in the occupied territories, despair and unrest grew. There was "something in the air"; many saw war approaching. "If only a leader," they prayed, "could rise to break the chains that shackle us."

Then came 1910, and with it two important Polish anniversaries: the five-hundredth anniversary of the Battle of Grünewald, in which Poland had finally conquered her most dangerous enemy, the Teutonic Knights; and the hundredth anniversary of the birth of Chopin. They were different events, but both observances called Paderewski home.

Many years earlier, on the borderland, Ignace used to beg the grandfathers and his father to tell him again the glorious story of the battle of Grünewald. None of these teachers of history guessed what project was shaping in their young listener's mind. His plan was that he would some day earn enough money to pay for a fine monument that would commemorate the victory of Poland's King Jagiello at Grünewald.

It was years before he had money enough, or time enough, to carry out his plan. Finally he was able to commission Antoni Wiwulski, a talented young Polish sculptor who needed encouragement and money, to make the statue. It presents the victorious Jagiello mounted on a horse; he wears armor, but his sword is at rest. Below the horse other figures picture four battle scenes. The monument was completed for the anniversary, and Paderewski traveled from Switzerland to Krakow to speak at the unveiling.

It was fortunate that Krakow was in the Austrian-ruled

part of Poland. Russian and German officials in the other two
divisions would not have allowed Poles so much freedom in
arranging a celebration. As it was, they didn't like the idea of
having this popular pianist come home to make a speech in
Krakow. They thought the Austrians much too easy-going
about this and other matters. What might Paderewski not say
to stir up trouble? The Germans and Russians sent agents to
watch and listen, while thousands streamed into the ancient
capital from every part of Poland, from beyond its borders.
Many arrived on foot, as pilgrims. They crowded about the
monument to read its inscription: "For the glory of our ancestors and the encouragement of our brothers."

The agents read it too. There wasn't much to object to in
the words they saw, though some asked, "What is meant by
encouragement?" Encouragement to do what? To rise
against their rulers? Not much chance. They turned away.
No, they couldn't find anything definite to object to.

Nor could they object to what the blond Pole who had
mounted the platform was saying. Yet there was something
in the way this tense multitude felt about Paderewski that the
agents wished they could put their finger on, something in the
way the crowd followed every syllable as this Pole stood
there, hatless, beside the monument, at times throwing back
his head, half closing his eyes as if to hold some vision clear
while his calm words fell on the hushed silence.

Calm words! For Poland's sake they had to be calm. Yet
people felt the immense surge of his faith. Beneath the free
sky, with a free wind blowing, they forgot rulers and agents.
Their feet were on that free soil they were sure Paderewski

saw, as his strong, melodious voice carried to the far fringes of the park.

"The achievement upon which we look today was not born of hatred," he said. "It was born out of deep love for our native land, not because of her present helpless state, but because of a vision of her bright and powerful future . . ." Magical voice, magical figure outlined against the black background of Poland's tragedy.

At this open ceremony, where agents of all three occupying powers listened, Paderewski guarded his words. But at a reception given him afterwards these daring prophetic sentences rang out:

"Brothers, the hour of our freedom is about to strike. Within five years, a fratricidal war will soak with blood the whole earth. Prepare, compatriots mine, brother Poles, prepare; because from the ashes of burned and devastated cities, villages, houses, and from the dust of this tortured soil, will rise the Polish phoenix."

"Within five years." This was in 1910. War broke out late in 1914. How was it that an artist, a man devoted to the piano, could see and hear the guns five years away? Remember that Saint-Saëns, long ago in Paris, had said, "Paderewski is a genius who happens also to play the piano." The keen brain, the swift intuition had from youth studied events, had grasped, in each of the world's great capitals, the meaning of what he saw and sensed. Had those capitals heard and believed his prophecy, the earth might have been saved from its blood-soaking.

Later in 1910 he returned to Poland to speak at a festival

at Lwów, which was celebrating the hundredth anniversary of Chopin's birth. Lwów lies in the same southern region as Krakow, but farther east, nearer where Paderewski was born. Because his arm had been injured Paderewski did not play the Chopin program chosen for this anniversary, but asked his American pupil, Ernest Schelling, to take his place. This was not an easy undertaking for a pupil, however gifted. But that day in Lwów the American satisfied both his teacher and his Polish audience.

Then Paderewski spoke, then listeners knew that Poland had its leader. After bringing to life the glory of Chopin's genius and character, portraying his suffering, his exile, he dared call to their faith and courage.

"Let us brace our hearts to fresh endurance, let us adjust our minds to action, energetic, righteous; let us uplift our consciousness by faith invincible; for the nation cannot perish that has a soul so great, so immortal.

"Let the oppressor hear, I do not fear him!"

He realized, others realized, that, with these two events in Poland, destiny was leading him in a new direction.

PART TWO

CHAPTER IX

Birthday Interlude

RIOND BOSSON, on the shore of Lake Leman, looks out across the water to snow-hooded Mont Blanc and a magnificent panorama of the Alps. On half the grounds are fir, beech, and poplar woods; on the other half spread the farm vineyards, fruit trees, pens for poultry and small animals, among them a sheepfold for offspring of a celebrated sheep presented to the pianist by the president of Argentina in 1911.

In the fine stone house, with its spacious sunny rooms, balconies, and terraces, two of its seven pianos—the two Steinway concert grands—stood in the long living room near a great window that framed lake and mountains. Grouped on them were inscribed photographs of persons distinguished in art and government, including one of Queen Victoria, sent after the Windsor visit. Portraits, the original Burne-Jones sketch, varied tributes, brought the world here. In the upstairs study were awards and decorations (Paderewski was one of the world's most decorated men), more photographs, and gifts: a long French table laden with music scores, an upright piano, prized objects of a Chinese collection which he had been gathering for many years. It was on this study door that the parrot, Cocky Roberts, knocked with his beak when practicing began. A friend who knew Riond Bosson well wrote: "The villa is filled from cellar to attic with priceless gifts. Popes and kings and men of high degree all give evidence of their great regard for this unusual man. State and municipalities and organizations throughout the world have registered on parchment, marble and bronze their appreciation of his genius. And the marvel of it is that the man remains unspoiled. He is as modest as a child, as unassuming as the humblest in the land."

The task of managing the villa was almost as heavy as if it were actually a hotel; merely to provide food for the stream of unexpected and expected guests was often a hair-raising responsibility, one Madame Helena couldn't carry by herself. Fortunately, she didn't need to, for sturdy, capable Antonina, left alone after an early unhappy marriage, had come from Poland and had shouldered the main housekeeping burden. It seemed wonderful to brother and sister to continue here their comradeship of the borderland.

On July thirty-first, feast day of Saint Ignatius Loyola, Geneva shops were stacked with boxes ready to be sent to Riond Bosson, with flowers ordered from faraway places for Paderewski's name day, which, according to an old Catholic custom, was celebrated on the feast day of his patron saint. During one name-day anniversary, Madame Helena pointed to piles of telegrams and letters on her desk. "No time yet, even to open them," she said, laughing, "or to arrange all the flowers."

Though Riond Bosson was a place filled with treasure, there was nothing in the least showy about it. It had an air of being constantly used, of being naturally open to friends;

some, indeed, who had little claim on its hospitality were welcomed when they appeared, often with their entire families, to "pay their respects." Added to these visitors were the music students, many from the United States, to whom Paderewski had promised criticism, or even a few lessons. His friend Sigismund Stojowski, one of New York's outstanding piano teachers, made a custom of arranging every four years a musicale at which his most successful pupils played only compositions by Paderewski. Paderewski tried to be in New York for these concerts and listened attentively to the young performers. Occasionally one whom he singled out for special approval was quick to ask, "Could I play for you later in Europe?" Some of the criticisms and lessons, added to an already exhausting day's program, were Paderewski's answer to such questions.

Neither Paderewski's sister nor his wife approved of his teaching. To this day one American pianist chuckles as she recalls an incident after her first lesson in the magical study. She was elated; the master had asked her to stay for tea! She had started down the stairs when she saw someone with a Pekingese dog at her heels approaching the foot of the stairway. The pupil hurried, for this might be Madame Paderewska! It was she—but with no look of welcome on her face. She was wearing, like a necklace, a long, loose white chiffon band with an ear of corn attached to each end; she dangled the ears before the transfixed student. "I'd rather he would grow this than teach," was her acid greeting as she strode by and outdoors to the poultry yards.

When Paderewski seated the young American at the tea table, she was so overwhelmed with gratitude for the lesson and for this friendliness that she tried to find some small way to be of service. Then suddenly a wasp alighted on the jam. Here is my chance, she thought, and tried to capture it. But Paderewski stopped her. "No, don't kill the wasp. Let it live." She was silent before this other kind of lesson. She was to learn how central in the make-up of this musician was his love for all living things.

Visitors traveling by train to Riond Bosson arrived at Morges, a trim little town a mile away, on which Paderewski depended for many services. The streets were usually gay with flags; Paderewski's photograph was displayed in shop windows, especially at the time of the birthday festivities, when the Morges Hotel became a kind of annex to the musician's home. It was to this home that Paderewski returned after dedicating the monument at Krakow and again after making the Chopin address at Lwów. As the second decade of 1900 moved forward, he and his wife became increasingly attached to the place. The grounds gave each opportunities for relaxation as they developed their hobbies. It was a red-letter day in Geneva, a short motor drive away, when the first boxes of Paderewski fruits appeared on the market. His manager was said to produce the best peaches and grapes in Europe.

To be escorted by Madame Paderewska through her lakeside poultry yards was an Alice in Wonderland experience. On a warm day she would probably be wearing a white dress and broad-brimmed white hat that set off her dark eyes and hair. She would begin by pointing out the general plan: the central hexagonal house where scientific records of breeding, histories, and awards were kept; the rows of yards fanning out, separated by wire fences covered with climbing pink and red roses; the stone troughs and pebbled floors, kept always fresh and clean. In these yards strutted or reposed magnificent hens and roosters, blue, yellow, black, red, and multicolored, long-tailed and short-tailed; the flaming-combed and skimpy-combed. Suddenly a procession of tiny bantams of pastel shades, with pink fluffs spreading out above their feet, would step delicately along a tree-shaded path.

"Chickens? Yes, just chickens," Madame Paderewska would laugh as she turned to her special prizes: a handsome russet that Queen Elizabeth of Belgium had sent, an orange-colored cock from China, a gray Polish variety that she had developed.

Along the Riond Bosson lake shore lay the properties of writer and musician friends, among them that of the Polish pianist Josef Hofmann. The members of the Fronzaley Quartet lived across the lake and often dropped in. This neighborhood group had the main responsibility of arranging the famous name-day frolic, each time a new entertainment, yet all alike in one thing: whatever the program, it must be a complete surprise to Paderewski. When there had to be a swift late rehearsal, he was locked in his room until everything was ready.

A visitor arriving at night, when the main spectacle took place, first saw roadside hedges, trees, and balconies ablaze with Chinese lanterns; then, in the light on an open doorway, the hosts, welcoming a troop of guests—many, especially the young people, in Polish costumes. On one occasion, when a modern symphony of excruciating noises was performed in the pianist's honor, he was obliged to sit in the front row and not clap hands over ears, while the Fronzaley Quartet and other noted musicians played—on cheese-graters, egg-beaters, typewriters (one man had a bath hose coiled around his neck for a horn), and many other contraptions—the ear-splitting movements of this offering. The director, scarcely noticed, stood behind a barrel into which at the end he crashed flower pots and crockery, and, as a grand finale, plunged himself head first! He was extracted, and with a magnificent flourish and flowery speech he presented the original red-ribboned manuscript of this work of genius to Paderewski, who rose solemnly to accept it. Then a Polish pianist read with painful seriousness an address on the many thousands of never-before-appreciated sounds from which such modern composers draw their effects.

Afterward, groups of young people danced a mazurka for their host, a polonaise, and various other Polish measures. He joined one line after another as they serpentined through the house, and finally, with Madame Paderewska, he led the way to the dining room, where a traditional Polish feast was spread: elaborately decorated ham, fowl and fish, aspics and salads, fruits, ices, many little cakes, and champagne. Next, the company whirled out to the garden for fireworks, for more jokes, more dances, recitation of poems, and singing.

There was another anniversary entertainment, one entirely Chinese in character, which has taken its portentous place in the history of a fateful year. Villagers of Morges arrived to enjoy the lantern-lit scene. Many came hiding anxious thoughts, for this was July 31, 1914. Inside the house, too, people tried to conceal a tension they could not escape. A sense of foreboding darkened the festival.

They went outside, and across the lawns saw a great paper dragon approaching, spitting fire. Within only a few hours that fiery dragon became for all the symbol of events already casting their shadow over this house, this lake, this Europe.

Soon after midnight, one, then another, of the Swiss guests was called from the supper table to the telephone. They had brought mysterious satchels with them to the party, and now disappeared to return in uniform and hastily say good-by to their host and hostess. They were off for their posts on Switzerland's frontier. Germany had declared that a "state of danger of war" existed.

Through these tense hours of August first, those who stayed on at Riond Bosson waited fearfully. Did this mean war?

CHAPTER X

August 1914

As the clock hands turned, that fateful August first, the piano remained closed. The dogs seemed strangely aware, huddled under tables and chairs. The telephone rang continuously with reports and questions. Terrified people begged for advice. How could they and their families escape the net spreading around them? Madame Helena and Antonina went from room to room, putting things back in order, arranging meals, not only for the few who had not fled from the party and who feared they might be held, perhaps for the length of the war, away from home, but for others arriving from all directions.

Paderewski had been up all night; there were dark hollows under his eyes. As the clock hands slowly turned, friends urged him to go down to his grape houses or orchard, even to the terrace, for a moment's relief from the unendurable waiting. But it was impossible, even for themselves. Each wanted to keep close to the telephone, the door.

"Look! Out on the lawn!" a woman cried. There gardeners, just as one would expect, were gathering up fallen rocket sticks, burned-out lanterns, the dragon, the remnants of the gay fête. But in the gloom of this August first the picture

became a strange symbol of destruction, of the end of happiness. Those watching the gardeners shuddered.

Paderewski was everywhere, alert to each word, with one question in his mind: What will this war, if it comes, mean to Poland herself?

Among the neighbors and friends, one man understood better than most what was about to happen. Again and again he and Paderewski drew chairs close as they talked and peered beyond the moment.

"*Voilà*, we have both known it must come. Yet we seem completely unprepared." Paderewski took an old map from his pocket, spread it on his knees.

His friend ran his finger around the border of Poland before it was divided, then down the lines that cut it into three parts. "Was any country at any time in history so trapped?"

"No. Two gigantic armies of Germany and Russia, about to fly at each other's throats, will do so across this divided body." Paderewski's hand swept across the map. "They will force Poles in each of these three divisions to fight against Poles in the other divisions, brother against brother."

"In the beginning, yes. It's bound to be horrible. But we must look further ahead."

Paderewski put the map back in his pocket. "Never forget that across the agony we must endure, the wind of freedom blows. While Poland's jailers fight one another their captives will escape. The three broken pieces will come together again."

"You can be certain of that, Paddy." A few intimates had given their friend that affectionate nickname.

"Yes!" He leaped to his feet, as he always did when deeply moved. "We shall see the rebirth of my father's, my grandfather's country! But, my friend, it will rise only from cities strewn with fallen roofs, only from blood-soaked fields."

At ten minutes past seven that evening Germany declared war on Russia.

"Why?" an appalled world asked.

To which Germany replied, "Because Russia is prepared to make war on us. It's a question of who moves first. Therefore, we move against Russia and her ally, France, against all her allies."

"But why?" the world still asked. That "why" has not yet been clearly answered. History takes a long time to sift out true explanations. But whatever the immediate reason, Germany's action was one more violent thrust in her age-old frenzy to push to the east, in that *Drang nach Osten* which centuries had failed to quiet.

A few days later, in this house that already hummed with war work, Paderewski was standing between the living room's two concert grands, with their array of photographs of kings and statesmen, looking out from his mind's darkness across the evening lake to the miraculous afterglow on the snows of Mont Blanc. People were always begging him to rest. But he found more rest in a few moments' contemplation of a mountain, a tree, of some transcendent beauty such as this, than he ever found in mere inactivity.

A neighbor stepped up beside him. "Suppose you had been caught inside Poland, instead of here in neutral Switzerland, where you are free to come and go, free to act?"

He whirled around. "That could not be!"

"No. It looks as if destiny has assigned you a task and seen to it that you are free to perform it."

Mysterious words. But each man understood the other.

And as we look back at the boy in the Polish village poring over his few histories, learning pages from the books of Poland's patriot-poets, listening to living history taught by his father and grandfather; as we watch him on world journeys, quitting the piano to seek out men who could best explain what their governments wanted and were actually doing, we realize that he had from the beginning been preparing for this hour.

No one could forsee the magnitude of the war. But even at its start men and women staggered before the picture their minds conceived. Guns, tanks, and soldiers were moving like chess men to points picked by the war lords.

Paderewski could not hope to influence that game. What then could he do? How could one Pole on the sidelines, a pianist, help seize from this onrolling horror his country's freedom? The task was gigantic. In most capitals Poland as a nation had long been forgotten. But not in Turkey. There, whenever the roll of represented countries was called and ambassadors answered "Present," Poland was always called as if it still existed, and an official would reply, "Absent." Turkey's unfailing reminder that Poland still lived further strengthened the bond of closest friendship between these two countries.

Poland was indeed "absent" from the thoughts of most of the world. Even her language had been suppressed, so that few besides Poles understood it. Paderewski more than any other man realized how immense was the need for education, the tremendous work that must be done, before his country could win justice.

While he questioned, "What can I do?" Russian and German armies swung back and forth across the Polish plains, seized millions of heads of cattle, more than a million fine horses, all other animals, all milk and grain. If one army missed a cow or a bin of wheat, the other found it. A terrible necessity stood out clearly. Hundreds of thousands of children, women, the aged, would die of hunger and disease unless somebody got food and medicine to them. Paderewski was tortured by the thought of what his friends in Warsaw, Krakow, and Zakopane were suffering. What was the plight of the Kerntopfs, of Edward? Had Russia conscripted the boys? He cried aloud as he pictured a pile of wounded and dying in opposing uniforms, groaning and cursing, and learning in their anguish that all were Poles.

He decided to organize a relief committee. A group of Polish exiles, most of them old men, gathered in his study. Chairs were pulled up around the long French table with its piles of neglected scores, while he walked back and forth, head bent, hands clasped behind his back. He had been working all day on his relief plan.

"We must move faster." He stopped at the end of the table. "If we can show other countries a competent head committee in action we can be sure more will be formed to work with it, once we show that food, medicine, however little, are actually getting in to the starving."

"But that's just what we're helpless to do."

"Not if we'll forget our differences and act as one man." This started a clamor of argument. He had hit the nail on the head. If Poles themselves would first get together, give to the world, which was too apt to say, "You'll never see harmony among Poles," an example of united effort, their task would be easier.

Only a world citizen like himself could get a true view of the cause of this apparent disunion. What else should one expect? Boys who grew up under Russian rule, as he had, were naturally more ready to believe Germany if, to quiet dangerous unrest, she promised something. Those who suffered under German oppression might more easily listen to Russia's false promises. Those brought up in Austria's section knew that Austria was less brutal than the other two conquerors. Politicians at the courts of all three had made it their business for almost a century and a half to foster dividing confusions.

Paderewski knew that beneath these divisions burned the same patriotic flame. "Be certain, we *will* get bread and clothing in to the starving. But first we must find a committee chairman, a Pole known in every country, to whom all will be glad to trust their money."

"What about Joseph Conrad? His *Lord Jim* and other books are read round the world. He writes such perfect English that most people have forgotten he is one of us."

"But he lives in England."

"Madame Curie?"

"She lives in France. The relief must be directed by a Pole living in a neutral country. The best-placed neutral country is Switzerland."

"Exactly." Paderewski stepped to the window, looked down the starlit lake toward Vevey. At Vevey lived Poland's

Nobel Prize winner, Henryk Sienkiewicz, author of *Quo Vadis?*, adored by all lovers of thrilling stories.

Friends read Paderewski's thought, it was their own. "Sienkiewicz!"

"But will he give up writing his history of Napoleon's campaigns, the book he came here to write? He can't run the committee and write."

Was there the twitch of a smile on Paderewski's sensitive mouth? Chairs scraped back. If he could persuade Sienkiewicz his plan had a chance.

No persuasion was needed. Suddenly how unimportant seemed the history of other wars! Sienkiewicz threw his book aside; he was never to write another great book. "I accept, my friend, this chairmanship. We will work together."

That was a beginning—Poland's greatest writer and Poland's greatest musician, completely dedicated to the Polish Victims Relief Fund. Vevey and Riond Bosson seethed with activity. To all Poles Paderewski's door was as open as his purse; his house served as headquarters for men coming and going on tasks for Poland, as a home to refugees. Many war victims from other lands appealed to him. His golden concert tours had provided for this. Now he was spending a small fortune each month.

His wife was everywhere, on the icy lake shore at dawn planning for birds, dogs, poultry. Her breeds, perfected by scientific labor, would be invaluable to Poland, once there *was* a Poland. "I will start classes and train girls to run up-to-date poultry farms," she said, as she and Antonina moved from one yard to another. Her head hummed with plans for future work side by side with her husband. Then she would hurry back up the slope to the house, to bandages and socks, stacks of mail.

Paderewski hadn't realized, when his sister came to live with them, the full extent of the part she was to play. Now Riond Bosson's dawn-to-midnight activities couldn't go forward without her. She had an executive mind and Slavic energy. Strangely, things seemed to be fitting into a pattern. As soon as her brother's Swiss relief committee was working smoothly he would have to leave, to start others in France, England, and the United States. She would carry on.

While he prepared to go he snatched time to study. Others might think he had studied enough; he knew better. Books and periodicals littered his study and bedroom. He often stopped, while dressing, to turn quickly to the exact page at which he had left off; friends were astonished by his ability to do this, and for a few minutes to concentrate on the next page.

He knew French almost as well as Polish, but for weeks he had been taking extra lessons, determined to be completely in command of this language whose use now might mean life to the desperate. For the same reason he took more English lessons; he practiced, as carefully as if he were exercising a finger, to rid his tongue of its slight lisp. In brief, he did what he had always done: he decided how he must prepare for the best possible performance of the task before him; then, like an athlete he went into training.

It was now mid-January 1915. Under his and Sienkiewicz' direction some food, some medicine, some clothing were reaching Poland's all but hopeless women and children. He and Madame Helena were about to start for Paris; their luggage was at the station. With a dozen dogs leaping in front of them, they made a last round of farmyards and orchards, said good-by to their pets, shook hands with their loyal workmen. Antonina was in charge at Riond Bosson. As the three stood silently in the doorway for a moment the same question burned in the mind of each. What would happen before the two returned? None of the three guessed that the return was five years away.

CHAPTER XI

Paris and London Again

PASSENGERS climbed down to face closed gates and guards in uniform; with strained faces they fell into line, passports in hand. For one important reason or another each sought to enter France, across whose northern cities and farms the thundering western war zone curved, whose capital, art-loving Paris, was Germany's objective. Paderewski believed that no necessity could be more urgent than his.

As the slow line moved, men realized how much they owed the clear-sighted people of the little country they were leaving, which had managed for so long to keep out of the world's insane wars, which had so freely shared with the oppressed, the world's exiles, its democracy, liberty, peace.

"What would Poles have done without Switzerland?" Paderewski touched his wife's arm. "You remember how many of our poets and scientists have found refuge here? Kosciuszko, after helping Washington win American independence, came here to die. The list is long. No Swiss will molest Riond Bosson while we are away; all will help Antonina to run our refugee home. All will stand back of Sienkiewicz and the relief work."

"Yes, may Swiss democracy and neutrality endure as the snows of Mont Blanc!"

They had reached the inspection desk. At last papers were stamped, gates passed.

Now they were speeding westward, through blacked-out cities, toward Paris. The French were struggling to care for their wounded and suffering; how could they help others outside? Paderewski believed they would find a way.

He had heard of an amazing accomplishment. Northern France, occupied by Germany, was the western battlefront; millions of people, women and children, the ill, the aged, were doomed to horrible suffering, as were millions in occupied Belgium, unless through a wall of steel and flame food could be got to them. Someone had broken through that wall; warring enemies, in the first agreement of its kind in history, were allowing a neutral United States committee called the Commission for Relief in Belgium and Northern France to carry a certain amount of food and clothing to ruined regions and distribute it to the civilian population.

The name of the man in charge of this undertaking—where had he heard it? Suddenly he saw, in a California town, two worried college boys standing before him! He chuckled as he told his wife the story of the half-empty concert hall in San Jose, the dashed hopes of two Stanford students. "One of those boys," he laughed, "is making a better relief director than an impresario!"

His face quickly saddened. The golden miracle of wheat was pouring in behind the western front, where men's pity centered. But how could forgotten Poland hope for the help given to the better-known countries?

As in his career as musician he had never deceived himself, so now he did not. He faced the situation squarely. It called for a tremendous work of education, one that began with "A B C" classes. As he grappled with this problem he fixed his mind on what must be arranged first—the formation of a Paris committee for his own small relief organization. A good one, linked with Sienkiewicz' head committee in Switzerland, was soon set up.

And there was something else to do in Paris. Another Pole, the economist Roman Dmowski, was there, working on another all-important need; he was trying to get scattered Poles to bury their political differences, to pull together under a *national* committee and to make the national organization strong enough to demand, out of whatever settlement followed this war, the best possible terms for Poland. Paderewski had long talks with Dmowski. They must not interfere with each other's plans.

In London the musician went to the Alma-Tademas, as he had in concert days, finding immensely heartening the loyalty of these old friends and of others who rallied around him in the familiar house. Here was no need for "A B C" classes about Poland, especially not for the painter's daughter Laurence, who, fifteen years before, had sat quietly stitching in the studio while her father and mother and Queen Victoria's daughter painted portraits of Paderewski, patiently posing in the carved chair.

The Alma-Tademas saw the same loved figure: the glorious red-gold hair, the electrically blue eyes, the strong hands; but in the face was a deeper beauty. Now it was not a matter of a portrait to be painted; the problem was how to collect money, medicine, and bread for starving people. Laurence, her dark eyes glowing, was the first to say, "I know it can be done." She became chairman of the English committee. So ardent was the effort of this intelligent group that within four months in London—already driven by its own needs—two hundred and fifty thousand dollars were raised for the relief fund.

While this work went forward, Paderewski was having a very different time trying to start the educational work. Politicians didn't want to hear about Poland's rights, especially from a musician, no matter how famous. As the busy horses of London's little hansom cabs hurried the world's best-known Pole, wearing a derby hat that looked amusingly small atop his magnificent hair, from one discouraging interview with some government official to another, people on the side-walks often recognized him and stopped. Paderewski! But no concert was advertised; what then was Paderewski doing in London? After seemingly fruitless effort, he himself was likely to say, "Yes, what indeed am I doing in London?"

But he went on trying to arrange for interviews. He knew how important it was for him to talk with Britain's Prime Minister, the stocky little Welshman, David Lloyd George, who seemed to know little and to care less about Poland—who seemed, in fact, to know alarmingly little about the whole situation in the east. In the beginning, the Welshman seemed to delight in opposing this Polish artist's arguments with a kind of scornful humor. He laughed at the picture of a free Poland.

Very different were Paderewski's meetings with his philosopher-statesman friend, dark-haired, dark-eyed Lord

Balfour. As in early days in their long conversations about world affairs, Lord Balfour still believed that Poland would win back independence. But that was a hope for the future. The task at hand was to save Britain's boys, if they could be saved, to win this appalling war. Yet he promised to do what he could for the Polish people. "So far as I shall have the power to bring it about," he said, "I promise Poland freedom."

Paderewski seized his hand. He felt crushed by the weight of the burden his friend carried. "Before this war ends," he said, "we Poles will be helping you."

Mercifully there was one great people whose back was not bent under the war load. When Paderewski left Riond Bosson his objective had been the United States, country of his boyhood's dreams and his manhood's marvelous realizations. Now that he had accomplished all that he could at present in Europe, he took passage for the Atlantic crossing.

The air was filled with rumors of Germany's plan to attack passenger vessels, as happened later when her submarine sank the *Lusitania*. But Paderewski paid little attention to warnings. If something had to be done, one did it. Fortunately he could now board a ship without dread of seasickness. Since his first hideous trip, he had crossed the Atlantic either to or from New York more than thirty times.

Despite the sinister battle-gray aspect of the whole port, the heavy anxiety in all hearts, English friends were determined that the Paderewskis' embarking on their mission should have a bright departure. Their cabin did not lack the customary fruits and flowers, books, and papers with the latest bulletins from the front. As the boat glided seaward, Ignace and Helena in their steamer coats leaned from the rail, waving handkerchiefs to Laurence and the others who were waving theirs. As long as they could be sighted, white signals flashed between the two at the boat rail and the group on the dock. White handkerchiefs waving! When would a white flag of truce float above the most horrible battlefield in history?

CHAPTER XII

The San Francisco Speech

THE customary band played. Brisk stewards in bright-buttoned uniforms circled the deck with familiar trays of hot soup at eleven o'clock and tea at four. But there was a new discipline aboard; it was felt with the first life-boat drill, when each person hurried, strapped in his life belt, to his assigned small boat, wife and husband to separate ones, silently climbed in, took his narrow place, ready to be lowered over the side of the ship. Yet one was free to come and go, to stay on a lightless deck all night, if he wished. Paderewski often paced the top deck, pondering, planning.

Day after day, with beautiful power, the ship rode the gigantic January swells, steadily lifting and dipping. Then, suddenly, the ocean, as if to put man and his toys in their place, took the boat in its teeth and shook it as a terrier shakes a rat. Man was put in his place, humbled before immense forces, still unconquered, like those unconquered forces of the mind that still herded human beings to the slaughter field.

With each hour, most passengers felt, the ship put the war farther away. Yet already Paderewski believed that the approaching peaceful port of New York would not escape the fires left behind. One day the flames would leap the Atlantic.

At a corner of Fifty-fifth Street and Fifth Avenue stood a

quiet, comfortable hotel. There the Paderewskis went; the Gotham was to remain for some time their headquarters in the United States. They found their apartment bright with red and white flowers, the round table of concert days reserved in the dining room below. Paderewski had always invited his manager, secretary, and piano tuner to dine with him. Again an intimate family of helpers would join him. And only four blocks up the avenue, where Central Park begins, were trees under which to walk. The whole world had so changed that it seemed almost as if he were in New York for the first time. Yet, perhaps better than any other foreigner, he knew and loved this country where he in turn was better known than any other foreigner, and had the friendship of many of the citizens directing its course. Some might think the task he faced not too difficult; in fact, he alone understood how endlessly difficult it would be.

The United States had declared neutrality, and, in government offices, observed it. But along the streets people seemed as violently "pro-Allies" or "pro-German" as those on the opposite side of the Atlantic. This was not surprising; men had been Americans so short a time, as history counts time, that the embers of old hates and loyalties of their mother countries could scarcely fail to be fanned into flame by the war hurricane. But this situation made it all the more imperative that Paderewski should, in word and act, scrupulously respect the official neutrality.

An appeal for relief would not trouble it; the United States was deep in relief work in Europe. But actually he had to make two appeals, and in each keep his position sharply clear. He represented no government; there was no Poland yet. He represented a desolated, starving people, victims, and here was the neutral rock on which he stood, of both sides. But how could he, except by telling their story, when Americans knew practically nothing of the Polish people, arouse sympathy, get food for them? Moreover, while not for a moment forgetting the American position, he must so tell the story that a way could be paved for later official support of his second, vastly more important political appeal for justice, a statesman's undertaking on which a pianist had embarked.

He had to move slowly, knowing exactly where each step led before taking it, even though his countrymen's cry for bread rang in his mind, even though their suffering tore his heart. He realized only too well how one group or another would urge him to hasty action. Indeed, in these very first days they crowded the hotel lobby, waiting to get to his door, to ask or more often to give advice. His secretary had an overtime job arranging appointments.

"If they were only other Americans," Paderewski burst out one day, "and not Polish-Americans, who are so sharply divided, the situation wouldn't be so complicated!" Poles had formed several organizations, either for relief or for political ends, but mostly they were working separately. Now, as various factions brought him their differences, he said frequently, "Let us talk in the park; things look clearer in the open air."

The music critic Waldo Frank, who happened to see one of these out-of-doors conferences, set down a verbal snapshot impression of the scene. "One saw him of an afternoon," he wrote, "walking in Central Park. Already the millions of Poles had made him their leader. He strode silent between

gesticulant friends. His hands were clasped behind his back.
His hair was still the music-lion's mane. Upon it, incongruous,
was a derby hat. Why did the hat seem to mock the magnificent hair?" [1] This sort of question was asked by countless
persons who think an artist's head is no place for a business-
man's hat, that no artist can be something else at the same
time, least of all a statesman. That mistaken belief was the
dragon this musician had to kill daily.

The year 1915 was crowded with practical business: first,
the hard task of getting Polish citizens themselves to pull
together for relief under the Polish Victims Relief Fund and,
for other purposes, under the national committee, directed
from Paris. His friend, the beloved Polish opera singer Mar-
cella Sembrich, had done much in New York to prepare the
way for his own work, which he pushed with such skill that
each week brought successes. But men, in particular politicians, continued to ask, "What can a musician know about
national affairs?"

He was not prepared to find the pleasant-mannered secretary of state, Robert Lansing, one of these. He went hope-
fully down to Washington to call on him and report conditions on the eastern front. He came away greatly depressed.
Mr. Lansing later admitted how unjust had been his first estimate of this artist's practical abilities. Indeed, to Paderewski
that office in the old Department of State building across the
street from the White House rang with "What can a *pianist*
know?"

But this was no time for discouragement. As he walked

[1] From *Time-Exposures* by Waldo David Frank, New York: Boni
& Liveright, 1926, p. 42.

slowly down the long flight of steps, looking across at the beautiful lines of the white colonial mansion, he thought reverently of the man inside, who had suddenly been given the fearful responsibility of leading the United States' one hundred and twenty millions on a perilous road. What would I not give to go now, today, to talk with President Wilson, he thought, as he stood several minutes before turning to his car, watching the Stars and Stripes floating in the wind above the White House. I must wait.

It was precisely men like Lansing, in official positions, who must be made to see that the time was near when they could use their influence to end the "greatest political crime in history." And there was one man more important to him than any other whom he must meet; not, to be sure, an official, but one who, strangely, understood better than any other American what lay back of this terrible war. This was a silent Texan, Colonel Edward House, who had been often in Europe, quietly studying what he saw, and who now lived in New York on Fifty-third Street, only a few blocks from the Gotham.

While beginning the delicate task of interviewing officials, Paderewski was at the same time getting ready to launch his public appeal for relief. From the hour they landed, he and his wife had been gathering dollars for the Victims Fund. Her Polish-costumed dolls sold fast. Then, one morning, Paderewski said, "I have decided to start west. Or, rather, it has been decided for me. There's a great opportunity; the San Francisco Panama Pacific Exposition wants me to give a concert in its huge auditorium."

"But you're not giving concerts." She lit his cigarette.

He smiled. "They know that. I am to follow my own plan: speak, then play, or play, then speak. I shall speak first."

"Thousands at that exposition. What a chance!"

"I wish I could be as certain of the result. Yet I can think of no place so lovely, so promising, as San Francisco's exposition beside the Golden Gate in which to make this first speech." He took her hand. "I've worked on what to say, passage by passage, as I would on the phrases of a concerto. I could judge how people would receive the music; I can't know how they will listen to my talk."

A nervous uncertainty gripped him as they unpacked in the accustomed rooms reserved at San Francisco's Palace Hotel. Presently Mr. Bruce Porter arrived to discuss the concert program. Paderewski played snatches of Chopin. "Would you like this? Or this?" As the hands raced over the keys the design of the program developed.

Fired, elated, Mr. Porter hurried to the exposition hall. There his enthusiasm waned as he took in the enormous, barracks-like place. He knew that something had to be done; at least a Polish flag could be hung on the bare back-stage wall. He suggested this to Mrs. William H. Crocker, as people who wanted things done in San Francisco in those days were likely to do. Mrs. Crocker ordered a flag made, which, when placed, fell from ceiling to floor. So glorious a white eagle on so widespread a red field had never before been seen; from the rear of the great hall the piano looked a mere black spot against it.

When Paderewski reached the stage and his glance swept across it, his throat tightened. What an incredible banner, magnificent symbol of promise! He walked to the front of the stage. A welcome that matched the flag shook the air, followed by a tense hush of expectation.

Quietly, his voice beautifully modulated, he began "I have to speak to you about a country which is not yours, in a language which is not mine." Newsmen, quick to catch a striking line, planned to flash this one over the wires. What had he packed into that first sentence that so electrically stirred the listeners? What overtones of suggestion the few words carried! Yet some in the audience waited guardedly, wondering if he would attack the side with which they sympathized.

Then, stroke by stroke, he proceeded to paint on an immense canvas, the historical picture, unknown to most, of Poland's long, largely peaceful struggle for the liberty of the individual. He described those early victories, in the 1300s and 1400s and 1500s, by which the Polish people won their charter of human rights and early established themselves as a self-governing republic, with elected kings. He traced the history of those splendid centuries when this republic was the freest state in Europe, the state in which the greatest degree of constitutional, civil, and intellectual liberty prevailed, a state that stood as a refuge for the oppressed, the persecuted, of other countries, a striking exception to the more militaristic monarchies of that time.

The vast crowd was listening as one person. Many were asking themselves if this man was not even more gifted as orator than as a musician. Yet he was using none of the artifices of oratory. He stood squarely on his heels, making few gestures, only occasionally raising his hand for stress or pause. He talked, as he played, with complete honesty and directness.

He was trying to present his country as he knew it, with faults and weaknesses, yet a passionate lover of liberty, a breeder of men like Kosciuszko, who crossed the Atlantic to help Washington in the American fight for freedom. Many American cities had raised statues to Kosciuszko; there was one in the park in front of the White House. But no city in imprisoned Poland would be allowed to raise a statue to him.

He had to move swiftly; he was compressing the whole story of a people into a half-hour's talk. He described the time when the three imperial knives slashed across the body of Poland, and three conquerors believed it severed forever. Then he told of the struggle, secret and ceaseless as their breathing, by which his people, his father, he himself, from that day to the present, had kept alive faith in deliverance, only to find themselves now caught in the iron jaws of a war not of their making, with millions homeless, starving, sick, and dying.

"Give me seed for this trampled, wasted land, bread for these starving." We who were there leaned forward, sitting on the edges of our seats, our minds lifted to understanding and compassion. He had done his best. But even as he turned to the piano to let Chopin's music express those Polish longings and ideals that escape words, he thought of things he had forgotten to say. San Franciscans who have heard Paderewski play a dozen times still insist that they have never since heard Chopin played as on that day. At the end the storm of applause would not be silenced until he sat down to give an en-

core. He chose Schumann's well-known *Warum?* Op. 12
No. 3. But instead of its tender query, a mighty, rebellious
question was thrown, it seemed, at the stars. *Why?* the music
cried. *Why* Poland's long martyrdom? The concert closed
on that question.

His San Francisco manager, Mr. Selby Oppenheimer,
rushed back stage. "Magnificent! Mr. Paderewski, never before have you played so gloriously!"

"That's hard to believe, for all the while I was tormented
by thoughts of the other things I might have said while I
talked."

For Paderewski the great Polish flag was an inseparable part
of that appearance in San Francisco. He asked if he might
have it, to carry on his tour from state to state. San Franciscans were delighted. On his new mission, as he returned to
American cities, to every one of the states, to speak at workmen's clubs, universities, concert halls, to small groups or to
thousands, he was reaping a harvest of good will. Though
most listeners could not have explained what gave Paderewski
such power as a speaker, after each talk more Americans
understood the "greatest political crime in history," understood what Poles so passionately asked of this war. As people
left a hall, one heard such words as these: "High time! Think
of it, that crime is as old as the United States. Just as we won
our freedom, Poles had theirs stolen from them."

Arthur Woods, New York's chief of police, probed
deeper. Genius, he said, is a quality of the soul. It expresses
itself in one way or another, but it is always greater than any
means of expression; that is its mark. This is the genius we feel
in Paderewski. Back of all his art, whether he plays or com-

poses or speaks in any of the various languages he is such a master of, one sees, through his supreme art, the genius of a great soul.

With each gift added to the Polish Victims Relief Fund, one more contributor felt a bond between himself and a far-away people. Congress passed resolutions expressing sympathy. President Wilson, by proclamation, set January 1, 1916, as a day for giving to the suffering Polish people. Paderewski could well feel that he was succeeding with relief work. But how far had he advanced in his more important effort to win the understanding and support of those few men on whose "yes" or "no" not bread but freedom for Poland depended? Scarcely at all, he admitted, at the end of 1915.

"That road seems barred. I'm at a standstill," he said one day in deep discouragement. "Until I meet a certain man, I shall remain so."

Then something happened.

CHAPTER XIII

The Beginning of Two Historic Friendships

EARLY in 1916 the mysteriously silent Colonel House of Texas returned from a trip around war-shaken Europe to his New York apartment. Only a few blocks separated Paderewski from the man who understood the European disaster, the man closest to President Wilson.

Only a few blocks—it might seem that he could walk over to Fifty-third Street and ask to see Colonel House. But not so naturally could a meeting of such importance take place. Months earlier, Paderewski had begun throwing out lines, interesting those friends who might be able to arrange an introduction, but so far without success. Then one morning came a message from Washington, from Mr. Robert W. Wooley, director of the United States Mint, friend of a friend. He expected to be in New York in two days, and hoped to take Mr. Paderewski to call on Colonel House.

Nothing better reveals the strain of 1915 than Mr. Wooley's reception at the Gotham. He was glad to be the agent of a meeting between the two men, yet he was guarded for fear Paderewski might count too much on the outcome. He had not thought of what Madame Paderewska's reaction to his news might be and was startled by her excited greeting, her certainty that this meeting was to bring victory to Poland.

"I do not understand." The embarrassed Mr. Wooley turned to her husband.

In Paderewski's face he saw the same joy; and heard words more restrained, but of like meaning. For Paderewski had long felt that only through a "providential person," whom he must find, could Poland be liberated. For some time he had believed that person to be the mysterious American who wanted nothing for himself but only the best for his country and for all peoples. Now Mr. Wooley was taking him to Colonel House!

In the Colonel's small library with its many photographs of men in control of the destinies of peoples, the clear-eyed, quiet-voiced master politician and the brilliant, enthusiastic Pole talked together. Mr. Wooley sat on the sofa, Colonel House near his desk.

Paderewski did not take the chair offered him but paced back and forth as he bent his forces to the building of his argument. He felt that this half-hour held the greatest chance of his life. Still walking, head thrown back or lowered, strong hands stressing a point, he continued to plead for his country, while his host, except for an occasional quiet question, silently listened. Thirty minutes stretched to an hour, then beyond it; yet he was encouraged to continue. In his lively account of this hour Charles Phillips says that when Paderewski now asked for practical, quick help, for an American loan of a million dollars to Poland, Mr. Wooley objected.

"There is no Polish government; the United States can't lend money to a mere Polish National Committee in Paris."

"Can't, Mr. Wooley?" Paderewski exclaimed. "The United States can do anything. She promised to drive out Spain and set Cuba free. She kept her word. No other country in the world ever did such a thing. She won the Philippines by arms, and then paid Spain twenty million dollars for them. No other nation ever did anything like that! She joined other powers in suppressing the Boxer rebellion in China and then—"

"Let him go on," House said in a low voice to Wooley. "Don't interrupt him." [1] The Pole's logic and eloquence had already captivated the Colonel.

This Paderewski sensed; it was easier to go on, as he did with mounting fervor. Finally he stopped, lifted his hand in a simple gesture that said, "I have done my best. Poland's case hangs on your decision. Have I succeeded? What is your answer?"

Mr. Wooley thought he already knew the answer, as Colonel House rose. Extending his hand, the Colonel said, "I promise you to help Poland if I can. I believe I can." Who could measure the import of these words? The blood rushed to Paderewski's cheeks. He and Mr. Wooley returned to the Gotham. "I walked," Mr. Wooley said, "with a person changed in two hours from a man all but staggering under the burden he carried, to a man stepping buoyantly as a boy about to break into a run."

This was the beginning of one of the historic friendships of our time, of uncounted walks between the Fifty-fifth Street hotel and the Fifty-third Street apartment, when either

[1] Adapted from *Paderewski, the Story of a Modern Immortal*, by Charles Phillips.

the gray-eyed Texan or the blue-eyed Pole hurried to consult the other. Later Paderewski wrote to House, "It has been the dream of my life to find a providential man for my country. I am now sure that I have not been dreaming vain dreams." [2]

In the summer of 1916 Colonel House introduced his friend to President Wilson. He had advanced his peaceful battle line across the threshold of the White House, where from the beginning he had known Poland's victory must be won or lost.

On a sultry summer evening the Paderewskis were in Washington, invited to dinner by the President and Mrs. Wilson.

"How strange," Madame Paderewska exclaimed, "in this neutral capital, these lighted offices, this activity!"

For in the dingy, gray State Department building across from the White House—in offices of the members of War and Navy departments, of the Red Cross—night lights burned, typewriters clicked, men—many in uniform—hurried in and out.

Within the mellow walls of the White House there was an atmosphere of solemn tension. More than a year had passed since the *Lusitania* had been sunk and a hundred and twenty-four Americans lost; since President Wilson had sent notes of protest and warning to Germany. Slowly but certainly during that year the United States had been moving toward the brink of war.

However, dinner in the spacious wood-paneled dining

[2] *Intimate Papers of Edward Mandell House*, edited by Charles Seymour. New York: Houghton Mifflin Company, 1926.

room was gay enough, brilliant, with the pick of official Washington there. After it, when the men rejoined the ladies in the long, white East Room, with its two huge crystal-leafed candelabra hung from the ceiling, and its portraits of George and Martha Washington, other guests arrived.

Suddenly a whisper silenced chatting groups. Since the war began, Paderewski had given up playing, except on rare occasions for the relief fund. On the low platform at the far end of the room someone was lifting the top of the concert grand.

"Is it possible that he's going to play?" ran the question.

"Yes," an aide answered, "because the President has asked him to."

There was a rustling of silk, the faint scraping of heels, as guests found places in the rows of uncomfortable small gilt chairs brought in for the evening. Those highest in official rank moved farthest front, nearest the President and Mrs. Wilson, who sat in the middle of the first row.

The Pole was at the piano. Men representing countries long Poland's enemies bent forward to listen, as did men from countries long her friends. There was scarcely a person in this white room who did not understand in some degree the magnitude of the task Paderewski had set himself. Some were following with particular watchfulness. The German Embassy had already reported to Berlin that the fact that the United States was so well informed about Poland was due to Ignace Paderewski's work.

But tonight he was not thinking of the rows of important, watchful people in the uncomfortable gilt chairs. He was thinking of one man, wanting that one man to understand the spirit of Poland, as Chopin made it live. President Wilson was listening with bent head. The kindly eyes behind the rimless glasses looked not toward the piano, but downward. Though, technically, he knew little about music, those watching his face sensed his emotion as he followed the marvelous interpretations of Chopin numbers.

When Paderewski finished and came away from the piano to President and Mrs. Wilson, who stood waiting to thank him, he knew from the President's handshake and quick, warm words that Poland's cause had made another advance. Greatly encouraged, he returned to New York.

There, between flying speaking tours, he and Colonel House met, at hotel or apartment, early or late. "We pored over maps," House wrote, "his maps and mine, and together we traced what we thought should be a homogeneous Poland." To the Texan, Paderewski was not only the leader of American Poles, but, as scholar and statesman, first among all Poles. Later House wrote a brief but broadly inclusive article, "Paderewski, the Paradox of Europe," for the December 1925 number of *Harper's Magazine*. No more clear, exact, and eloquent estimate has been left to us; practically every American biographer of Paderewski has quoted from it.

"Before Paderewski came to the United States to devote himself to the Polish cause," House wrote, "the American Poles were divided by misunderstanding and suspicions. He gave to American Poles a single purpose . . . At the close of 1916 his countrymen in America without dissent chose him . . . conferring upon him the power of attorney to act for them and decide all political matters in their name. This document, unique in history, bore the seals and signatures of all the Polish societies in the United States."

This choice came in the nick of time. For on November 5, 1916, something was done that might have ended hope for a new Poland, unless opposed swiftly by a united people. The Germans proclaimed the independence of Poland!

Experienced persons took this for what it was—not a sincere offer of freedom but an attempt to make the Allies think that there was no longer a "Polish cause" to fight for. And, more important, if Germany could win despairing Poles to belief in their offer, would they not flock to the German Army to help win its war against France and her allies?

Yet Paderewski realized that many Poles might not see this, especially those at home, so war-tortured that they were ready to snatch at even an imitation olive branch held out to them. Desperately worried, he knew that he must act at once. American Poles had given him the power to speak for them all. He would. Three million Poles in the United States would at once refuse to accept the German offer. That word would encourage Poles outside the United States to take the same swift action.

War insanity had grown to something more terrible than any remembered human disaster. To many, Poland's cause seemed such a small item on the list of issues that they would have found it easy to cross it off that list. But always Paderewski and his work stayed their hands. Daily the influence of the United States on the outcome of the ever more vast struggle became clearer. As 1916 closed, the eyes of the world watched President Wilson's every move. And close to Wilson they saw the pianist-statesman, Paderewski.

In this November the President was up for re-election. A change of leaders in so critical an hour might well be disastrous to Poland, for in the sympathetic understanding of House and Wilson lay her best chance for justice. Paderewski now proved his political skill, as he swung practically the entire important Polish-American support to the Democratic ticket. This meant that in at least three key states with large Polish-American populations, election day would roll up decisive majorities for Wilson.

November sixth the President spent at Shadow Lawn, his country home in New Jersey, to await there the result of the voting. Early that morning, having been told that Mr. Wilson wished to thank him for his work during the campaign, Paderewski drove down to Shadow Lawn. He was shown into the pleasant study, where he found the President still looking more like the scholarly Princeton professor he had been than like a man in politics, just finishing a pile of European telegrams about Germany's latest move. Paderewski felt the warmth of his quiet welcome.

Wilson turned quickly to the subject uppermost in the minds of each. "What is the meaning of the German offer of independence to Poland?"

"It is an attempt to win Polish soldiers to strengthen the German army. It is an attempt to cut off the Allies' support from Poland!" As they talked it was clear that Paderewski was voicing the President's own conviction.

The time was short. Wilson wanted to hear as much about Poland's past and about her future needs as could be crowded into it. He listened, thoughtful and absorbed, while Paderewski, with eloquence that poured from his inner being, rebuilt his country's past, showed its need for what it had so long possessed—a strip of the Baltic coast, with a seaport through which goods could come and go. Poland could not live, economically, as a corked bottle. It must be able, as in the past, to send products down the great Vistula River to the free ocean. The justice of this claim the President completely recognized.

They talked of Wilson's belief that after this war ended somehow out of it must rise a new Europe, dedicated to the ideal of human brotherhood. The long, narrow face, the kindly eyes were lit up by the vision of a new order, in which men would settle differences, not by murder, but by peaceful negotiation. Wilson already saw Poland as one of a brotherhood of nations. What drew him to this Pole—what attracted every man of vision—was the fact that Paderewski saw not only that part of the human picture that most concerned himself, but the whole picture, and asked justice for all peoples; here was an ardent patriot thinking in terms of the brotherhood of man. So they talked, while the President's fate—and with it Poland's fate, his visitor believed—was being decided in voting booths across the country.

The hour's visit was over. As the two walked to the hall Woodrow Wilson stopped, and, in a solemn, grateful good-by, said, "My dear Paderewski, I can tell you that Poland will be resurrected and will exist again."

The patriot went back to New York where he would not sleep till he heard the election returns.

Late that night newspaper extras cried Wilson's defeat. Paderewski was stunned. "This can't be true," he said brokenly.

At five o'clock the next morning wires flashed a denial of the midnight report. Western states had swung the victory to Wilson, assuring his second term. The terrific tension of the night was cut; Paderewski could now snatch a few hours' sleep. Then with zeal he resumed his work of speaking and playing.

CHAPTER XIV

The United States Enters the War

SCARCELY two weeks later Paderewski's work was interrupted by news from Switzerland. Sienkiewicz, Poland's magical storyteller, whom he had left in charge of the central relief committee at Vevey, was dead. He felt his own burden become heavier. As he watched 1916 draw to its dark close, across the devastated Polish plains spread indescribable misery; in the west bloody battles along the Somme shook the windows of Brussels.

In this same darkness began 1917, the year so fateful for the United States. On the afternoon of Monday, January eighth, Paderewski was practicing for a widely advertised relief concert when word came that Colonel House would like to see him. He was soon in the intimate study.

Here is his own account of what passed between them. "On Monday, January 8th, 1917, Col. House said to me, 'Next Thursday I am going to leave for Washington and I wish to have with me your memorandum on Poland.' Terrified by the suddenness of that request, I exclaimed: 'But I have my recital tomorrow. I shall not be able to hold a pen in my hand for two days, and besides it is impossible to prepare such a document without having the necessary data.'

" 'I must have the memorandum Thursday in the morning,' he answered, and it was the end of our conversation. I immediately returned to the hotel and spent four solid hours in preparing the program of my recital.

"Only on Tuesday, after the recital, could I turn my mind to that new, very heavy task. It took me over thirty-six hours of uninterrupted work to prepare the document which was delivered as requested, on Thursday, the 11th, at eight o'clock in the morning.

"Led by purest, the noblest idealism, Colonel House, whom I shall never cease to consider as Poland's providential man, made our cause his own cause. He pleaded it with all the ardor and generosity of an American heart. When about a week later I called on him, he was in a cheerful mood and said, 'The President was very much pleased with your memorandum. Now get ready. The first shot will be fired very soon, and it will take your breath away.' " [1]

It did. He was speaking and playing in the South on January twenty-second when the President, on Capitol Hill, delivered his grave message in person. On the twenty-third, in a Southern paper, Paderewski learned that Woodrow Wilson had done what no leading statesman in one hundred years had dared to do: he had dared to talk of a "new Poland."

"No peace can last," Wilson said, "or ought to last, which does not recognize and accept the principle that governments

---

[1] From Paderewski's address at the dinner given in his honor by the Kosciusko Foundation, New York, May 16, 1928, and printed in the Foundation's volume, *Ignace Jan Paderewski 1918–1928.*

derive all their powers from the consent of the governed, and
that no right anywhere exists to hand peoples about from
sovereignty to sovereignty as if they were property. I take
it for granted . . . that statesmen everywhere are agreed
that there should be a united, independent, autonomous
Poland."

Tears blurred Paderewski's eyes as he read. The battle was
not yet won, but this was indeed a mighty shot fired, not for
Poland alone but for the whole deceived, despairing world.
Everywhere men lifted their heads, as this new fearless voice
sounded above the war madness.

February and March passed. Paderewski whirled to and
from New York on his relief mission. No three men in the
world were working harder than he, Colonel House, and
President Wilson. The President, while he worked, pondered
day and night the question of how out of the chaos of war
a new order might be born, a brotherhood of nations pledged
to live according to law, policed and directed from within.
He did not, alas, see the European picture as it actually was,
or he would have known how long it must take to put out the
fires under the seething cauldron where boiled the hates—
religious, political, ethnic—of two thousand years. While
he labored, things were happening that brought him hourly
nearer that awful decision he had, in the beginning, determined to avoid.

On the last night of March, Wilson felt definitely that the
end of peace was at hand. He was restless in his bed, got up,
went out on the south veranda of the White House, taking
his little typewriter with him. Mrs. Wilson heard him, went

quietly to the kitchen, brought him a bowl of milk and crackers, and left him.

There in the early morning he wrote his war message. All day it was with him, and he considered it carefully, perhaps changing it here and there. He sent for his friend Frank Cobb of the New York *World*. Cobb was delayed in coming. At one o'clock in the morning, he found the President in his office.

President Wilson had a way of summoning Cobb to Washington, but Cobb rarely spoke of these visits to the White House. Since Wilson's death two of Cobb's associates, Maxwell Anderson and Laurence Stallings, have written down their memory of his recollection of one such occasion which is history. Here is Anderson's account of what Cobb told him:

"Old W.W. knew his history. He knew what wars were fought for, and what they do to nations that wage them.

"The night before he asked Congress for a declaration of war against Germany he sent for me. I was late getting the message somehow and didn't reach the White House till 1 o'clock in the morning. The President was waiting for me, sitting in his study with the typewriter on his table, where he used to type his own messages.

"I'd never seen him so worn down. He looked as if he hadn't slept, and he said he hadn't. He said he was probably going before Congress the next day to ask a declaration of war, and he'd never been so uncertain about anything in his life as about that decision. For nights, he said, he'd been lying awake going over the whole situation; over the provocation given by Germany, over the probable feeling in the United States, over the consequences to the settlement and to the world at large if we entered the melee.

"He tapped some sheets before him and said that he had written a message and expected to go before Congress with it as it stood. He said he couldn't see any alternative, that he had tried every way he knew to avoid war. 'I think I know what war means,' he said, and he added that if there were any possibility of avoiding war he wanted to try it. 'What else can I do,' he asked. 'Is there anything else I can do?'

"I told him his hand had been forced by Germany, that so far as I could see we couldn't keep out.

" 'Yes,' he said, 'but do you know what that means?' He said war would overturn the world we had known; that so long as we remained out there was a preponderance of neutrality, but that if we joined with the Allies the world would be off the peace basis and onto a war basis.

" 'It would mean that we should lose our heads along with the rest and stop weighing right and wrong. It would mean that a majority of people in this hemisphere would go war-mad, quit thinking and devote their energies to destruction. The President said a declaration of war would mean that Germany would be beaten and so badly beaten that there would be a dictated peace, a victorious peace.

" 'It means,' he said, 'an attempt to reconstruct a peace-time civilization with war standards, and at the end of the war there will be no bystanders with sufficient power to influence the terms. There won't be any peace standards left to work with. There will be only war standards.'

"The President said that such a basis was what the Allies thought they wanted, and that they would have their way in the very thing America had hoped against and struggled against. W.W. was uncanny that night. He had the whole panorama in his mind. He went on to say that so far as he knew he had considered every loophole of escape and as fast as they were discovered Germany deliberately blocked them with some new outrage.

"Then he began to talk about the consequences to the United States. He had no illusions about the fashion in which we were likely to fight the war.

"He said when a war got going it was just war and there weren't two kinds of it. It required illiberalism at home to reinforce the men at the front. We couldn't fight Germany and maintain the ideals of Government that all thinking men shared. He said we would try it but it would be too much for us.

" 'Once lead this people into war,' he said, 'and they'll forget there ever was such a thing as tolerance. To fight you must be brutal and ruthless, and the spirit of ruthless brutality will enter into the very fibre of our national life, infecting Congress, the courts, the policeman on the beat, the man in the street.' Conformity would be the only virtue, said the President, and every man who refused to conform would have to pay the penalty.

"He thought the Constitution would not survive it; that free speech and the right of assembly would go. He said a nation couldn't put its strength into a war and keep its head level; it had never been done.

" 'If there is any alternative, for God's sake, let's take it,' he exclaimed. Well I couldn't see any, and I told him so.

"The President didn't have illusions about how he was going to come out of it, either. He'd rather have done anything else than head a military machine. All his instincts were against it. He foresaw too clearly the probable influence of a declaration of war on his own fortunes; the adulation certain to follow the certain victory, the derision and attack which would come with the deflation of excessive hopes and in the presence of world responsibility. But if he had it to do over again he would take the same course. It was just a choice of evils." [2]

The next day Woodrow Wilson appeared before Congress and read his War Message.

Two days later the Senate passed the war resolution; four days later the House passed it.

On April sixth, what Paderewski had foreseen happened; the war sucked in the United States.

Horrible as it was to see another nation, one he loved, drawn into the carnage, he could not but rejoice for Poland. Her cause would be immensely strengthened with the United States actually fighting with the Allies. His own task would be simpler.

"Now there's a chance for my army!" In their hotel living room he and his wife were talking over their changed position. "I shall wear a groove in the State Department steps till I get permission to raise my Polish army for training camps and guns."

"Yes." Madame Paderewska filled the tea cups. "But rest if only for a week before you begin. It would be different if you could drop one thing for another, but you simply add each new work to the load."

[2] *Cobb of "The World."* A Leader in Liberalism, by John L. Heaton, New York, Dutton, 1924, pp. 267-70.

"Naturally, and the arithmetic will continue. Another cup, please. We must think about the Kosciuszko army."

"But first, in this pile is there no letter from Morges?" Madame Paderewska spread out letter sheets in Antonina's firm handwriting.

They leaned over them, reading together the report of growing needs of their refugee home, its Red Cross work.

"You see why the arithmetic must continue. If it weren't for Antonina's clear head and quick hands how far would the money reach?"

"Here's something," Helena continued. "Dogs and horses are fine, and the chickens—she doesn't forget that we want to hear this too. The trees are trimmed and in good shape; our men are faithful." They looked from the letter with misty eyes. How lost in the past were those rich days with trees and pets, troops of friends, music!

Many Poles were already serving in the Allied ranks; more would form part of American forces. But to cause the world to think of Poland as an independent country, Paderewski wanted to organize Poles above the draft age into a Kosciuszko Division, to fight on an equal footing, side by side with the forces of other Allied armies. "That separate body will tell the world that there is a Poland," he said. "I must print Poland on men's minds before boys and girls will be able to find it again mapped in red or blue in school geographies."

It was a brilliant plan. But at first every leader whose help he had to have was against it. However, his countrymen were not; when he proposed it at a Pittsburgh meeting of the Society of Polish Falcons they thundered approval. And now with stubborn patience he tried to obtain from France and the United States permission to go ahead, which finally he won.

The more closely men followed him, the more amazing they found him. Gray had begun to streak the red-gold hair, lines to furrow the broad forehead, but the eyes' blue was still electrically vivid. There had been no slacking in daily gymnastics, in the regime to keep the body fit; he looked youthful in his easy-fitting clothes and low, narrow-brimmed brown felt hat as he now tackled the job of organizing an army corps. One thing that kept him young was his saving sense of humor. It was a rare day that was not lightened by a laugh. Years later, at a New York banquet given in his honor, he could see the amusing side of even this long toil for his Polish army.

At a testimonial dinner in New York he said, "We owe it to the marvelously gifted statesman who within a few months converted this peaceful democracy into a military power of the very highest order. Though overwhelmed with work, he always had a kind word and a friendly smile for someone molesting him with the same matter at least twice a week. If you do not guess who were the molested and the molester, then I confess, with a very slight touch of repentance, to having so frequently and so mercilessly bored your former secretary of war, Newton D. Baker.

"It was terrible boring, and very deep too, but I got oil, anyhow!"

At last two training camps for Polish volunteers were opened, near Niagara Falls—one on Canadian soil, one in the United States; and the registration of volunteers began. Soon there were twenty-two thousand enlisted men, and Paderew-ski faced the problem of getting them across the Atlantic.

This took him again to Washington, where the secretary of the Navy, Josephus Daniels, sent him to a young assistant, Franklin Delano Roosevelt. And once more he reaped the benefit of an old admiration. Ever since Mr. Roosevelt had heard Paderewski play, this pianist had been to him one of the world's greatest figures. He quickly arranged to transport the Paderewski troops to Europe, where they were joined by many more. Nearly one hundred thousand men were turned over to Poland's brilliant soldier, Josef Haller, who had been chosen to be their general.

Then something happened that profoundly moved Pade-rewski. He was honored by this body of volunteers who wrote the name "Ignace Jan Paderewski" on the roll of every company. Daily, when it was called, one hundred thousand answered, "Present."

So, with the white eagle flying and "Paderewski" inscribed on each regiment's roll, the separate Polish army, symbol of a free people, took its place on the western front.

Secretary Daniels wrote of his own and of the president's admiration and affection for Paderewski:

When I lunched with Wilson he said, "I wish you could have heard Paderewski's speeches for his country. They compared with Patrick Henry's famous 'Give me liberty or give me death,' and I could understand how the self-contained Jefferson was so moved as to light a fire of liberty in his heart that was never extinguished. I knew Paderewski was a master of harmony, but as we heard his eloquent appeals for his country I felt that it was in victory that he had touched chords more sublime than when he moved thousands as he commanded harmony from the piano."

Exactly one year after he sat thirty-six hours preparing the paper on Poland which Colonel House took to Washington, President Wilson announced to a joint session of Congress his Fourteen Points—his plan for a peace settlement. For one day this war must end and a peace treaty must be made. Then men would have their chance to build better than they had before. Beyond the roaring guns, the putrid trenches, the world heard what Wilson thought the fourteen great foundation stones should be.

As Paderewski read Point Thirteen he saw what he had been trying to print on men's minds set down by a man to whom all peoples listened. Point Thirteen was Poland's point.

"These are practically my words," Paderewski said, his voice shaken.

An independent Polish State should be erected which should include the territories inhabited by indisputably Polish populations, which should be assured a free and secure access to the sea, and whose political and economic independence and territorial integrity should be guaranteed by international covenant.

So much had been won. What more was there to do until this war ended and the peace conference began?

There was plenty! Even with the United States' help, could the Allies be certain of the war's outcome? Poland's enemies would not accept Point Thirteen. Her friends were busy with many urgent matters. Paderewski couldn't allow himself to count for one hour on these victories along the way; there could be no rest until the final goal was reached.

But before 1918 was over, on the eleventh of November, armistice guns boomed the end of four years of mass murder. The long, horrible strain had pushed people to the verge of breakdown. As they felt it snap they did silly things. They screamed and wept and sang wildly; threw bits of paper into the air; drank whisky; danced along the sidewalks; ran to dig up buried household treasure; got fire hoses to wash streets clean of the enemy! But they also knelt in the churches. This was a first, surface reaction. The few who carried the major burdens were thinking of the enormous task ahead. Paderewski was among these. With his mission in the United States accomplished, he must return to Europe, where the Peace Conference would meet, where Poland's future would be decided. On December fifteenth he arrived in Paris.

From Paris he crossed to London. He longed to go home to Morges, even for a week; it wasn't far. But he dared not take that time off. After each talk with a key man he saw more clearly that the great stumbling block in Poland's way was the frightening but understandable fact that Poles themselves were not yet united. There was the Polish National Committee in Paris, led by Roman Dmowski, which was recognized by the Allies as the official representative of the Polish people. But there were other committees of Poles in other places, each insisting that it was the true spokesman for Poland.

It was his friend Arthur Balfour, Britain's powerful foreign secretary, who now helped Paderewski to make his next big decision. They had been talking about Poland's chance for a seat at the peace table; of how unlikely it was that she would get one unless some kind of stable Polish government that represented all important factions could be organized at once. For a minute or two the two men sat in silence, facing this stupendous necessity.

Then Balfour, according to Colonel House, advised Paderewski to go to Poland to organize a concrete government so that such a government might send representatives to the forthcoming peace conference and have a voice in determining questions relative to Poland.

"I will go," Paderewski said, "but on one condition. I must travel on a British man-of-war."

"A warship?" This had not occurred to Balfour. It seemed all but impossible to arrange. He made several other suggestions.

But Paderewski stuck to this condition, explaining why. He was not thinking of personal dangers, though they were still real. But it was of the utmost importance that he should arrive with all the prestige of a British ship flying the victorious Union Jack. He went home to await the decision.

All day and all night he waited. Then a member of the Foreign Office arrived with this message: "I have to notify you that your wish has been granted. The name of the cruiser is the *Condor*. It will sail in two days from Harwich."

"To venture into Poland at this time," said Colonel House, "was a perilous undertaking for one who had played so important a role in the humiliation of the governments of which the new Poland had so recently been a part, and to make the venture through Danzig was particularly perilous. But fear for himself had never been a part of Paderewski's character." [3]

Paderewski rushed to Paris, to report to Dmowski and the National Committee, then back the next day to London. He had landed in Europe on December fifteenth. Four days before Christmas, having hurried off a letter to his sister and presents for all helpers at Morges, the Paderewskis boarded the British warship *Condor*, cautiously beginning to cut its way through the mine-sown North Sea, with a British mine sweeper policing the dangerous path. Both warships headed for the Baltic and Poland's ancient seaport, Danzig.

[3] From "Paderewski, the Paradox of Europe," *Harper's Magazine*, December 1925.

CHAPTER XV

First Days in Poland

THE battle-seasoned cruiser wound slowly eastward between mine fields. The Paderewskis had a small cabin, against whose porthole gray swells broke. They ate at the captain's table, where the two men sat long after each meal was finished, talking about the Navy's work in these bleak important northern seas, about Poland and what must be done there.

Ship officers enjoyed their novel duty of carrying this famous pianist and even more famous patriot, this lovable, tawny-headed Pole, safely to his new task. One day they invited him to their wardroom for a smoke. There he noticed a battered piano against the wall, such a dismal wreck of an upright—with twangy strings, one pedal broken, a half-dozen keys completely out of commission—that no one would have dared refer to its presence. Besides, they knew that in 1917 Paderewski had determined not to play again until his work for Poland was finished.

Suddenly, in the midst of story-swapping, he got up and headed across the unsteady floor toward the piano. "Would you like me to play for you?"

Would they? But on *that?* He laughed, and began. For two hours they sat spellbound, while incredible music floated out

from the drab battleship into the December night. How he
accomplished the miracle they said they would never understand. If they could have felt his aching muscles the next day
they would have had at least part of the explanation.

At Copenhagen the *Condor* picked up smartly uniformed,
quiet-mannered Colonel Wade, chief of the British first military mission to Poland; also a young Pole, Sylwin Strakacz,
who, though no one in the group foresaw it, was to play an
important role in the Paderewski drama.

The British Foreign Office had asked Paderewski to deliver
its letter of instructions to Colonel Wade. The two men
tramped the deck hour after hour, talking about what lay
ahead. They realized they faced dangers on entering Poland
from the west; by an armistice arrangement the German
Army had not yet evacuated that territory.

Companionship on the *Condor* at this time, when the men
were thinking wistfully of home, was pleasant. When, on
Christmas Day, the ship docked at the drab port of Danzig,
once the gold-façaded, sail-flecked Venice of the North, as
he said good-by Paderewski took off his gold wrist watch and
presented it to the captain. They made a sizeable party as they
stepped from the landing ladder; Colonel Wade and the
group of Army officers with him, two Naval aides; the Paderewskis and a personal aide and secretary. They looked at the
port, sea-bordered and river-crossed. Above every house in
Danzig a red flag cut the mist.

"Christmas banners!"

"Yes, but actually they are the red flags of the German
Socialist Party, which seized control of the Danzig government shortly before the armistice."

Poles pressed toward them, overcome by emotion as they welcomed the "savior" of their country. No Danziger Germans came; they weren't welcoming a man who had arrived to establish freedom and peace in Poland. And most of the citizens of this port, after over a century of foreign rule, were Germans. For a long period before Poland's seizure, grain and salt, copper and furs, and the other export wealth of Poland's rich territories had been floated down the broad Vistula to Danzig, and thence out to the Baltic and farther waters. And in through Danzig had come products vital to the inland plains.

As they drove to a hotel for the night, Paderewski turned to Colonel Wade. "You are looking out through the ancient window of our race."

"Well, it's a pretty dreary, boatless port today. But"— Wade pointed down a street—"there's gilt of past grandeur on every house front. Wasn't it about the most important city of the old Hanseatic League? I wish there were time for a look at its huge old warehouses and wharves."

Their first important stop was to be Poznań, key city of western Poland. They started the following day. Now, every hour, the situation grew more tense. German officers tried to prevent Paderewski's getting off the train at Poznań, but failed. There were scenes of ecstatic enthusiasm as a great crowd welcomed him. Yet the city was quiet; its Polish population knew that the eyes of the Allies were on them; they were pledged to keep order. The presence of postwar German troops, constantly trying to incite them to disorder that would discredit them, made keeping that pledge difficult. The next day there would be a larger welcome and a procession, which the party would watch from the Bazaar Hotel, where the Paderewskis had the front rooms and where conferences began at once.

That day, as a procession of ten thousand marching children carrying small Polish flags neared the hotel, Prussian soldiers bore down on them, opened fire on the terrified line and also on the hotel windows. The children scattered. An aide ran to Paderewski's room, which was strewn with broken glass, and implored him to come to the rear of the hotel. In answer the pianist walked to the mirror hung between the smashed windows, still being peppered with bullets, and retied his necktie.

The procession was broken up, as the Prussians had meant it to be. But now no pledge could restrain the young Poles. Although they were without a commander, they quickly organized, and for three days hand-to-hand fighting raged about the hotel. They overcame the Germans and took control of their city. Many persons were wounded; one was killed. Later, Paderewski wrote Colonel House: "In Poznań, the day after my arrival, during the procession of ten thousand school children marching through the streets, some Prussian companies, mostly officers, opened fire upon the peaceful, unarmed crowd. Quite a number of shots were fired at my windows, some of them at the window of Colonel Wade. Explosives and dum-dum bullets were used. American and British flags were insulted; there is no doubt that the whole affair was organized by the Germans in order to create new difficulties for the Peace Conference."

The Paderewskis and Colonel Wade worked early and late through the last hours of 1918; then they left for the capital. And here began an extraordinary progress over a route covered with snow, marked by war wreckage of homes, trees, and bridges, along which, in the cold, great companies of people waited for the train. Paderewski made no less than seventeen speeches to weeping, jubilant crowds at stopping points.

He arrived at Warsaw station on New Year's Eve. Above the tumultuous sea of people the colors of countless flags, badges, and uniforms seemed to be blended into one vast banner of a reunited Poland. Even I couldn't have imagined it, he thought; if only my father had lived to see it!

The Warsaw station was the one that had been policed by the Russian invader's soldiers on the day when he and his father had climbed down from the freight train to search for the conservatory. Some of his old teachers were in the crowd, some of the Kerntopfs, many school friends. It was hard to keep his voice steady as he stepped forward to speak; but he did, because he knew that the fight was not yet completely won, Poland's frontiers not yet fixed by the Peace Conference. A singing, flag-waving procession escorted him to the Bristol Hotel, and for two days a hundred thousand people continued to celebrate his arrival. He knew that these thousands were better off than some—the starving and dying weren't celebrating—but it was good to have this hour.

Warsaw's situation differed from Poznań's. There were no enemy troops here. Though the German Army still hung on in the west, and Russia's Bolshevik Army threatened from the east, the capital was in the strong hands of Poland's soldier-hero, Józef Pilsudski. While Paderewski made his hard-won diplomatic gains outside Poland, this daring general, who at times used a desperado's technique, and had more than once missed death by a split second, grappled with the usurper inside Poland, organizing Poles into fighting units under the very nose of the enemy. He had little time or wish to think of Paderewski's diplomatic battle; all he wanted was the chance to "go it alone," as he tried to rebuild his country.

In November Józef Pilsudski had been declared chief of state and had set up a socialist, almost communist government, one that expressed in Poland the revolt of the working classes who before the end of the war had staged revolutions in Russia and Germany. However, there were already several additional political parties; indeed, to some onlookers it seemed that the malicious wit who once said, "Put two Poles on a sofa and you have a party," was not far wrong. The Allies asked if this workers' champion, Pilsudski—a revolutionist since boyhood, condemned by the Russians to servitude in Siberia, then held in German prisons, escaping always to continue to harry the enemy—could be persuaded to work with the conservative Dmowski, leader of the Polish National Committee in Paris.

Paderewski knew Dmowski well; he had not yet met Pilsudski. Of one thing he was certain: both men loved Poland. And of one thing the Allies were certain: they would not deal with *two* bodies representing Poland. Could Poland's greatest artist, believer in democracy, pull these split forces together? Colonel House and President Wilson believed he could; Herbert Hoover believed he could; Lord Balfour believed he could. All knew that only he could. And he himself on this first day of 1919 was confident.

He put on his long fur-lined coat and small brown hat, and drove under bare January trees to the Belvedere Palace, where Pilsudski lived—a spacious, handsome building, but with no corps of servants about. He was shown quickly to Pilsudski's study next to the bedroom, and was greeted by a man in rough soldier's uniform—a man with sharp, secretive eyes under bushy dark brows, a brush of stiff iron-gray hair above the broad forehead, an untrimmed mustache trailing over the strong jaw. Everything about him seemed to mock at the quiet elegance of his visitor's appearance. They sat down; Paderewski began his appeal for union. But as minute after minute passed, while Pilsudski nervously took and half-smoked one cigarette after another, Paderewski felt more and more sharply this iron man's bitter impatience at even having to talk about the Paris National Committee. Only the fact that Poland was bankrupt and starving made him listen at all; he knew that the Allies, who alone could advance money and food, had no confidence in his socialist government. Yet at the end of two ash-strewn hours, he remained completely against the idea of a government that would represent all parties—not only workmen, small shop keepers, soldiers, but conservative elements as well. All Paderewski's offers to co-operate personally seemed to fall on deaf ears.

Paderewski left the Belvedere exhausted, though not yet beaten, and returned to the Bristol Hotel, where his wife was deep in relief work. He did not need to report his failure. She and his staff heard it in his step in the hall.

"This is my major battle." He sank into a chair. "I've got to win it. But that will mean going through fire. There's sulphur in the air around that man!"

He didn't know that at that very time a group of hot-heads were plotting to overthrow the Pilsudski government. He did know that Poland's need for arms to hold Lwów against the Ukrainians was critical. So, with his wife and his young secretary, Sylwin Strakacz, he hurriedly left Warsaw for Budapest, to try to get munitions from the Allies. He got no farther than the first night's stop, Krakow.

There, at three in the morning, Strakacz waked him. "Marshal Pilsudski has sent his chief of staff to call you back to Warsaw immediately," he said.

"We are returning at once," Paderewski said. He was already almost dressed. As he traveled with Pilsudski's representative across the bleak, snow-covered plain back to the capital his thoughts raced. What was the meaning of this quick change? Had the marshal decided to allow a democratic government? He dared not let himself count on that.

CHAPTER XVI

Paderewski, Prime Minister and Minister of Foreign Affairs

HOTHEADS trying to overthrow his government were not responsible for Pilsudski's calling Paderewski back to the capital; it was something quite different.

On January fourth a few Americans had arrived in Warsaw. At their head was the Stanford University biologist Vernon Kellogg, a volunteer in the vast humanitarian undertaking set up by Herbert Hoover, the first of its scope in history. It was called the ARA—American Relief Administration. The American government stood behind it. To some it seemed only an attempt to aid others. Those who understood knew that in helping other peoples back to normal living the United States was at the same time serving its own people.

It was Poland's turn to be helped. Hoover sent Kellogg to Warsaw to work out the way. With him went Colonel William R. Grove and several aides. They arrived just in time for the plot.

This was Kellogg's report to his chief in Paris:

> The night after we got here, a little light-opera *coup d'état* was pulled off, with a little firing of rifles and machine

guns; one man was killed, six ministers arrested, but Pilsudski was left in charge as chief-of-state. Yesterday came the reverse; the ministers were freed and several heads of the opposition arrested. . . . Paderewski is expected back tomorrow morning. However, something may happen again tonight. In the meantime, the people here take it all quietly so far, and barring the shooting at night and a few machine guns in the streets, there is no sign of civil war.[1]

Kellogg's job was, first, to convince Pilsudski that only to the democratic government for which Paderewski was working could loans and gifts be made; that the socialists must cooperate with him. If successful, Kellogg was quickly to set up machinery for inflowing aid. He called on the chief of state the afternoon of his arrival to discuss starvation, disease, typhus, smallpox, tuberculosis. He called the next day, and again. The marshal was bound to listen with a different ear to arguments of an American empowered to start money, food, and cotton toward Warsaw.

On the morning of January seventh, three days after the Americans arrived, Paderewski was back in Warsaw and at once saw their chief. At noon he called on Pilsudski, who now agreed to help form a joint government, with Paderewski holding the double post of prime minister and minister of foreign affairs. But how deep did agreement go? Was he

[1] From the Hoover Institute and Library for War, Revolution, and Peace, Stanford University, Stanford, California. The documents, papers, and books of this library constitute the world's most comprehensive collection covering the period of World War I and that of the Paris Peace Conference. The author of *Paderewski* has had valuable assistance from Dr. Witold Swarokowski, curator of the Polish and Western European collections of the library.

accepting this Democrat with the intention of getting rid of him when it was safe to? No one searching the strong-jawed, secretive face for an answer found one.

In addition to this diplomatic work, Hoover's envoy hastily made a few practical provisions for Poland's new life. For instance, he obtained from a patriotic Pole his house, called "The Blue Palace," to serve as the United States legation and the home of its first minister, Hugh Gibson, who was to become one of the best friends Poland ever had.

The day before Paderewski got back, Kellogg rushed a message to Paris: "Because of horrible conditions among children and the sick, condensed milk should be sent instantly."

If it was hard for Americans to face what they saw, for Paderewski it was agony. These millions of skin-and-bones children were *his* children. These workmen staring at stripped, cottonless mills, at tracks with no trains, were his workmen. They would continue to starve and to stare if he failed in his task. But soon, by land and sea, from Europe and the United States, medicines, food, materials for all classes alike would begin pouring into Poland.

It was this practical argument that, more than anything else, opened the way for the United Republic of Poland. Paderewski could breathe more freely as he now conferred with Hoover's aide. Once he paused to recall with glistening eyes that California concert when he had asked a Stanford student-manager to report the extent of his financial disaster.

"Isn't it one of those simply unbelievable turns in the road of destiny," he said. "That bankrupt western engineering student now tackling the bankruptcy of my country—isn't it unbelievable, Kellogg?"

One night he arranged a gala performance at the opera in honor of the Americans where, in the box, Kellogg sat next to him. When the orchestra struck up "The Star-Spangled Banner" and the whole house was on its feet, all eyes on the box, suddenly these two men threw their arms about each other, unashamed of tears.

The professor, his job of starting things accomplished, left for Paris, leaving Colonel Grove in charge.

Within two weeks after the British ship brought him to Poland, Paderewski called a National Council of one hundred men, chosen from all three divisions into which the usurpers had cut Poland, and from all important parties. He picked these men, not for party reasons, but because they were capable of handling Poland's problems. This Council was to meet in Warsaw on January fourteenth, to set up the new government and arrange for a general election. They now asked him, as prime minister, to form a coalition cabinet of sixteen members.

To have proper quarters in which to work, he moved to Zamek Palace, the yellow-walled building before which, when he was a music student, he had so often stood, thinking of Poland's past, dedicating himself to her liberation. His wife moved with him to the Zamek where she had her private apartment next to his. Some persons didn't like this; they objected to having a woman too much in the picture.

He was in a desperate hurry to see the new state started, not only because of the tragic suffering of the people, but also because the Paris Peace Conference that would fix its frontiers

would meet in Paris on January eighteenth. Poland's other
delegate, Dmowski, was there; but as head delegate he, himself, should arrive by the eighteenth. Yet his most urgent job
was still here, where people had been prevented so long from
having any experience in government, and therefore from developing leaders. Nor could they train officers for an army.
With Poland's frontiers not yet fixed, a Bolshevik Army
threatening from the east, and a German one from the west,
how could the government stand? It had enough brave men
for defense, but lacked those who could organize and direct.
This made him all the more anxious.

And it made Americans send word to the Paris office, saying "The Poles want uniforms, munitions, officers for forces
to guard their borders against Bolsheviks and Germans," and
adding that nothing but the very remarkable spirit of all
classes could have saved the country from ruin during this
time; and that food relief played an important part in sustain-
ing that spirit.

During this hard January, while he labored, often till dawn,
Paderewski listened for some message of support from outside. It was late in the month and he had received none. Then
one morning Strakacz brought him a dispatch: "Here is
something, a dispatch from the American Secretary of State."

Eagerly he read:

Paris, January 22, 1919

To His Excellency, Mr. I. J. Paderewski, Warsaw.

The President of the United States directs me to extend
to you, as Prime Minister and Secretary for Foreign Affairs
of the Provisional Polish Government, his sincere wishes
for your success in the high office which you have assumed,

and his earnest hope that the government of which you are a part will bring prosperity to the Republic of Poland.

It is my privilege to extend to you at this time my personal greetings and to assure you that it will be a source of gratification to enter into official relations with you at the earliest opportunity. To render to your country such aid as is possible at this time as it enters upon a new cycle of independent life, will be in full accord with that spirit of friendliness which has in the past animated the American People in their relations with your countrymen.

Lansing [2]

"This is a staff in my hand," Paderewski said. He turned with fresh courage to such reports as this from relief workers: "People are walking at night because too cold to sleep. Clothing need almost greater than food need. Found old wreck of a man walking to a town twenty kilometers away for food, and women barefoot carrying packs, people working their way back through desolation to the place where they once lived."

"My God," he groaned, as he read. "We must hurry. Is all our own brave people are doing, all the help of the ARA more than a drop against this misery?"

A month later his secretary rushed into the office waving another telegram, and again tired, eager hands seized it.

Paris, 24 February 1919

Paderewski

I am glad to report that the stream of food from the

[2] *U.S. Department of State: Papers Relating to the Foreign Relations of the United States; 1919.* Washington, D.C.: U.S. Government Printing Office, 1934, Vol. II, p. 74.

United States to Poland has now reached Warsaw and so
far as one can humanly see, it should be of steady flow and
increasing volume. This will, I hope, be accepted as a tribute
not only to the Polish people but personally to yourself.
It is now four years since I first attempted in cooperation
with yourself to secure the international organization of
systematic relief to Poland and late as the day is, and great
as the suffering of the Polish people has been, yet I witness
this day with no little personal satisfaction. It makes a good
omen on the road of realization of Polish aspirations to
which you have devoted your life.

                                                    Hoover [3]

"Read it. I must hear as well as see it." Paderewski listened
with head lifted, eyes on the statue of Sigismund beyond the
window.

This was his reply:

                                        Warsaw, 15 March 1919
Hoover
    Your beautiful message touches me profoundly. I cer-
tainly remember all your noble efforts four years ago to
assist my country and shall never forget your generous
endeavoring, alas frustrated by the merciless attitude of our
common foe. It is a privilege for any man to cooperate in
your great work and I highly appreciate the honor of having
my name in a modest way associated with yours in the
present relief of Poland. The activity of Colonel Grove and
his staff is beyond praise, goods of highest quality arriving
daily and thousands of people, after four and one half years
of terrible suffering, realizing at last what wholesome and

[3] Hoover Institute and Library, Stanford University.

nutritious bread is. In behalf of the government I beg to offer my sincere thanks and with deepest personal gratitude, I remain devotedly yours,

I. J. Paderewski [4]

In April he decided that he could safely start for Paris, where Doctor Casimir Dluski, brother-in-law of Marie Curie, another noble Pole who gave radium to all people, had been substituting for him at the Conference. He had already asked the Allies to send a political and military mission to Poland to study conditions on the spot. The Noulens mission was sent, and it was in their special train when they returned to France that Paderewski, his wife, and his aides left Poland. The commuting had begun, at a time when long distances were still long distances. On this trip they started April second and arrived in Paris April sixth.

He was going to the meeting as the agent of a united Poland, but uncertainties tormented him: What will happen when I am away? Dare I count on loyal support? Had any other Prime Minister no sooner formed his cabinet than he had had to leave it to shift for itself? Will my enemies [despite his immense popularity, there were enemies] find in my absence their chance to strike at me? Above all, can I trust Pilsudski?

The train was pulling into the Paris station. Everything done so far had been leading up to what must now be done. He opened his briefcase. His quarters at the Hotel Wagram would be conveniently close to the meeting; the ordinary

[4] *America and the New Poland* by H. H. Fisher, New York: Macmillan Company, 1928.

sessions were being held on the left bank of the Seine River, in a palace on the Quai d'Orsay. As soon as he had set up his office he arranged to call on "The Tiger of France," Clemenceau, French minister of foreign affairs, and president of the Peace Conference. He had not yet met Clemenceau, though several other Conference members were old friends. On his way he may have smiled wryly, remembering the trouble Parisians had brought on himself by attaching to him, too, an animal's name; the former "Lion of Paris" about to meet the "Tiger of France"!

He expected to wait before the busiest man in the capital could see him. But in a few minutes Clemenceau appeared, and as he held out a gray-gloved hand in welcome, enjoyed a quip: "You are perhaps a cousin of the celebrated pianist, Paderewski?" The Pole, delighting in play no less than the Frenchman, bowed deeply as he said with mock solemnity, "I, myself, am Paderewski."

"Is it possible? And now, prime minister. What a fall!"

They laughed, and an important interview was under way.

Paderewski's duties might be new, but Paris was known to him and he to Paris. From the day of his arrival, pressmen and people on the streets watched for the pianist who had swept them off their feet in the golden concert days; they gathered where they thought he might pass, to cheer and wave. They found the "lion's mane" graying slightly, but his walk and look still young. Some asked why he didn't go back to his piano; hadn't he accomplished his great work? The world had other statesmen and politicians, too many of them, but no other pianist like himself. They wanted more music.

Ten men and their assistants, gathered around a table in the French foreign minister's office to write the peace treaty, had their own questions about the pianist, Ignace Paderewski. A few already believed in his ability as a statesman; others openly doubted.

CHAPTER XVII

The Paris Peace Conference

LIBRARIES of books have been written about what took place
in 1919, in that high-ceilinged, red-tapestried room on the
bank of the Seine River, where the Council of Ten (two
representatives of each of the five victorious "Big Powers" of
World War I) directed the rough course of the peace treaty.

At one end of the room, in an armchair pulled up before
his desk, sat the "Tiger of France," presiding over meetings.
High cheekbones and a drooping dark mustache gave this
cynical almost eighty-year-old Frenchman an oriental look.
He wore gloves (usually gray cotton ones) to protect himself
and others because his hands suffered from a skin disease.

To Clemenceau's right and left delegates sat in high-backed
chairs before their desks, surrounded by secretaries and aides.
The chief interpreter, directly at his right, translated into
French and English all speeches and discussions not made in
those languages. President Wilson and his secretary of state,
Robert Lansing, had desks at his left. One noticed at once
Great Britain's head delegate, the little Welshman, Lloyd
George, and the cultivated Orlando of Italy. The many
meetings in this room were called the small, or ordinary sessions. Here Dmowski had been chief spokesman for Poland
until Paderewski arrived.

Many nations beside the "Big Five" had a part in forming this treaty that would change the map of Europe. And when all delegates met, these full or plenary sessions were held at the Palace of Versailles, outside Paris.

Colonel House said of the Conference scene, "While the accredited statesmen occupied the center of the stage, influential men and women in every walk of life were there in some capacity. . . . They came from the four corners of the earth . . . never before in the history of the world were there such a variety of questions to be solved, questions affecting the hopes, the fears, the ambitions of so great a part of mankind. The Conference became a fiery furnace, and few survived its cruel and relentless flames." [1]

The Conference had been in session eleven weeks. Delegates were tired, disillusioned. Many saw their hopes for a peaceful world, in which near-sighted self-interest would give way to a broader justice, already doomed. The story of President Wilson's suffering was written on his face. Wisely or unwisely, he had acted as no American president before him ever had, when he left the White House to go to Europe to battle in person for the adoption of his "Fourteen Points," which set before a despairing world the goal of a different, better society. Point Thirteen proclaimed the rebirth of a free Poland. Not only Paderewski, who had had so vital a part in shaping it, but Poles everywhere, who felt the chains of a century and a half struck from them, looked to President Wilson with inexpressible gratitude, with reverence. Thus Paderewski was shocked to find the atmosphere

[1] "Paderewski, the Paradox of Europe," *Harper's Magazine*, December 1925.

of criticism and ill-will that had spread around the president
of the United States. About this time, an American woman
was in a train in war-ravaged Yugoslavia. Standing at one
end of the car a half dozen Serbs, of about college age, were
talking excitedly. Finally, one of them came to her seat,
apologizing as he said, "We have decided that you are an
American, and want to know if we may ask you a question."

"Certainly," she laughed. "But that doesn't mean I'll be
able to answer it."

"We are discussing your President's Fourteen Points. We
don't think we'll live to see them adopted. But we believe that
a great idea born in sincerity and faith will not die. Can you
tell us, was President Wilson sincere when he sent forth
these fourteen points? If he was, we can die knowing that
others who follow *will* see that different world."

Was President Wilson sincere? How easy to say an em-
phatic "Yes!" She was war-hardened, but when she saw the
light in the eyes of those Serb college boys as their envoy reported the answer, her own were misty. Incidents like this
one stood out against the attacks on Wilson.

Paderewski quickly let his friend know that he had arrived,
and the President at once asked him to come to his house. He
leaned on the warmth and confidence of this friendship. Their
visit gave new courage to each. As it ended, Wilson said he
would continue to press for acceptance of Point Thirteen
and for Poland's just frontier and territorial claims.

Dmowski was now so completely pessimistic about Poland's
situation that Paderewski refused to side with him; he
couldn't admit that it was too late to try to change it. At the
end of January, when his colleague had presented Poland's

case in a five-hour speech—her right to territories with a majority Polish population, to frontiers long hers, to the port of Danzig—both Clemenceau and Wilson had congratulated him. Dmowski enlarged this speech with two long notes. But the more he labored, the less was actually promised Poland, partly because his cold argument, however brilliant, didn't strike fire, also because his personality often made men dislike him, many because of his strong anti-Jewish attitude. Britain's leading delegate, Lloyd George, wouldn't speak to him if not obliged to. It was easy to see that all this worked against the Polish cause.

Here was a situation which could be changed only by a new, more human approach, perhaps only by Paderewski's genius for friendship. Closed doors must be reopened—and soon, for the Conference was nearing its end. Turning his back on worrying reports from Warsaw, Paderewski threw all his energies into a supreme effort.

One of his first interviews was one with Lloyd George, who had blocked the attempts by Wilson and Clemenceau to win support for Poland, and who laughed at Poland for thinking her pianist could hold his own with trained politicians of the Conference. After this first visit Lloyd George's attitude was less hostile; the more the two men saw each other the more friendly it became. It wasn't long before the Briton would give the Pole a tip about an approaching meeting where he might score a point.

One early event showed Conference members Paderewski the statesman, still unknown to most of them; though for years House, Wilson, Balfour, and a few intimates had thought of him first as a statesman. Now the French foreign minister gave a dinner in his honor. It was expected that in response to the toast the Pole would speak of his country's rights. Instead, he talked of Paris, so fortunate in having been chosen for this meeting with its opportunity to bring about a new brotherhood among peoples. Eloquently he turned their thoughts from individual ends to the general good. They listened intently while he called them back to the early purpose of the Peace Conference. A hush fell on the room; these dinner guests felt the love that flowed through him, love for all men. It was as if a wind swept away the fog of gloom that had gathered over them; they saw things again in a clearer light. And they realized that though he had made no appeal for his country, Poland had regained her place in the larger picture; that in spiritual power no delegate from the big nations ranked higher than Paderewski.

Members liked to discuss with him the larger problems of the meeting. For one thing, he knew European history better, perhaps, than any other member, and because of his extraordinary memory he had facts always ready for use; also his knowledge of languages made an interpreter unnecessary. Clemenceau often asked him to explain a French point of view to Americans, just as Wilson called on him to explain an American attitude to the French. Frequently, a delegate from some other country would exclaim, "Oh, if we had a Paderewski!" Indeed, in the minds of many he became a kind of representative at large for the smaller nations.

This growth in Paderewski's position and influence did not mean that the battle for Poland's claims could be easily won. To restore her frontiers meant changing those of neighboring Bolshevik territory, of Lithuania, Czechoslovakia, the

Ukraine. Naturally, all fought against change. Yet slowly he made gains. But as the weary meeting stretched out, in those last weeks before the document was handed on May seventh to the Germans to study, part of what Poland had won was lost. The treaty, signed on June twenty-eighth, brought bitter complaints not only from Italy, Turkey, and other nations, but from Poland because of Polish-Czechoslovakian, Polish-German, and Polish-Ukrainian border decisions. Paderewski's political enemies quickly charged him with each failure. His own disappointment was great, and he foresaw future trouble in any refusal to provide the new state with just frontiers; but he saw first one blazing fact: this treaty declared Poland to be again an independent nation. It was with this thought foremost in his mind that he went to Versailles to sign the peace treaty.

President Wilson's losses were more tragic. To save his plan for a League of Nations, he had had to make terrible sacrifices. He seemed a broken man. As few could, Paderewski understood his grief, and suffered for him.

In the Hall of Mirrors in the Palace of Versailles, a magnificent glittering room, delegates took their places one by one. Thousands of important "outsiders" had used all their influence to get an admission card, but only a lucky two thousand, including members, could have seats. As he took his place, President Clemenceau, seventy-seven years old, was heartily acclaimed for a tremendous task brilliantly performed. When all was in order he asked that the representatives of Germany be conducted to the small table where the parchment was spread, to sign first. It had not been easy for Germany to find men willing to sign for their defeated country. The Cabinet had resigned, others refused, but still others took their places.

Who, watching that signing, saw World War II only twenty years distant? Nation followed nation; there was loud applause for Lloyd George, for President Wilson. Then came Paderewski. People leaned forward to follow his every motion; he had, as always, dressed with care: long black morning coat, white waistcoat, white bow tie, smooth-fitting buttoned shoes. The applause was like that given only to the few preceding delegates of the "Big Powers," as he signed with a gold quill presented to him for this use. Some who have examined the parchment have thought his beautiful signature especially designed for this day. But for him how impossible would have been such seeking for effect! During a quarter of a century a letter, a message, a photograph carried that never-changing inscription, the "I" and the "J" generously looped, the small letters exquisitely written, the final "i" sweeping forward beneath the name, to its beginning, then back again; halfway there, curving into something like the lower clef signature of a bar of music, forming a fine support for the whole. For the treaty, a beautiful, impressive signature, but as he had always written it. Then he used a gold stamp that hung from his watch chain to affix his seal to the name.

CHAPTER XVIII

Growing Intrigue in Poland

THIS was the middle of 1919, which was to prove Paderewski's year of trial as by fire. How different the second half might have been, but for the dark shadow of Pilsudski cutting across it.

Always Paderewski had talked of the "straight road." Never side-tracked by self-interest, he had traveled a straight road toward the goal of human brotherhood. He saw his country taking that road. When, years later, he was asked to talk on a Victor record (little realizing that this would be his last recording) he still took as text "The right, the straight path."

Imagine his shock on returning to Warsaw to find the road criss-crossed by intrigue, by daily plotting to undermine what he was trying to build—a relentless campaign against himself, directed by a master hand. He was bewildered; he refused to believe that it could not be checked and turned. But he had first to give his whole attention to making clear to the government and the public why the Peace Conference in the end had rejected certain Polish claims.

Nothing now could stop Pilsudski's effort to rid himself of the man who stood in the way of his regaining full control of Poland. When, six months earlier, he agreed to a coalition government, he had done so because of the utter necessity of getting outside help against the famine and disease that were threatening to wipe out his people. Only Paderewski could win that support. In his mind he gave a surface consent; as soon as the worst crisis passed, he would drop this coalition business. He remained what he had been, a military dictator for whom the sword decides. No two men starting from the same base—love of country—could have stood farther apart in their ideas of how to secure the best good for that country.

Paderewski, open, aboveboard, believed that democratic action, even though imperfect, painful as it often proved for himself, was the only way to a better world. Pilsudski, as a Frenchman described him, was "shut tight, buttoned, screwed down," with no confidence in the time-wasting, cross-purpose methods of democracy. He was not interested in seeing Poland allied with western powers; he wanted no interfering advice from the west. Instead, he kept his eyes on the east, on Russia. Mentally he canceled Paderewski's promise to the allies (they wanted no further war on any front) that Poland would not attack the Bolsheviks, but would only defend herself against attack. He planned to strike against them, to free the people of Latvia, White Russia, and the Ukraine, who longed for independence from Russia. At the core of his policy was belief that if he could set up a line of neutral, federated states on Poland's eastern border, his country needn't worry about her future. His first step would be the conquest of Kiev. He did not launch this undertaking until after Paderewski had made a great decision, but the thought of it influenced his every move. The Prime Minister implored him not to take so appallingly dangerous a course.

The marshal replied by speeding up his campaign to un-seat his team-mate. It is needless to follow in detail the ugly picture. The pattern of political intrigue, of underground and above-ground scheming, is familiar. It was easy enough to increase confusion in the *Sejm*—the Polish Assembly—where normally there was always plenty because of its sixteen parties, all inexperienced. Inexperience turns a ready ear to intrigue. So, in this second half of 1919 the National Demo-cratic Party, with which Paderewski stood (though actually he had joined no party), could no longer rally enough sup-port to save him.

And now there were attempts to discredit his wife. These were given wide publicity through a newspaper article which represented her as an ambitious, interfering woman; ridiculed her hovering concern for the Prime Minister's health; said she prevented the right people from seeing him, and influenced him to make appointments harmful to the State.

This campaign was one more way of trying to shake the endurance of a chivalrous, sensitive man; for, though most people saw through the slander, once started it spread. Were it less serious, her husband could have laughed over the charge that his wife interfered in politics; he said that she wanted to leave the room and often did if a political matter came up; politics bored her! It was true that she sometimes interrupted a long-drawn-out private (not official) confer-ence to suggest that the Prime Minister and his friends must be exhausted, and invite them to her apartment for refresh-ments. He realized what he owed to this watchfulness, for which she was now blamed. People dislike a protector. Those who were kept from reaching their idol, the crowd after a concert pressing for a handshake or an autograph, seekers after interviews or favors, would-be pupils, and many others were quick to charge their failures to his wife, were ready to believe ill of her. Some to this day repeat the old exaggerations.

Paderewski knew that Helena asked nothing for herself; wanted only to help Poland's soldiers, children, and women; had orgainzed the White Cross for soldiers, homes for widows, agricultural and business courses for girls. Tortured by Poland's lack of relief supplies—clothing, anesthetics, and the simplest medical provisions—had she not in Paris given Marshal Foch no rest until he sent a train of thirty-seven cars loaded with necessities to Warsaw? While Paderewski stripped himself of his life's savings (personally paying salaries and expenses of all working for him) she, too, poured out her funds to augment the never-large-enough sums she collected for her ceaseless relief work. When he saw her in tears as she read the news article, he was cut to the quick.

Naturally people knew of her sacrificial devotion. But Pilsudski was succeeding in turning the tide against her husband; to ignore the good his wife accomplished, play up her mistakes, and invent others was one of the tactics. Playing up an irregularity in Paderewski's habits was another; he would not talk on the telephone (use of this instrument jarred his nervous system); he would not "take notes" (he had trained himself to memorize perfectly at sight); he started the day too late (usually he had to work most of the night, but often Pilsudski called him for a conference at two or three in the morning). Small minds fastened on small things. One petty criticism of his wife was more cruel than others. Certain persons resented what they called her "indifference," a vague, detached look in her eyes when they were trying to interest her in some project. Could they have seen, not many years ahead, this beautiful wife, by a tragic mental illness completely cut off from her husband, all life about her blotted out, they would have bitten their tongues rather than wag them in gossip.

The prime minister could fight back, but this would reveal to the world disunity in Poland, a revelation he was determined to avoid at whatever personal cost. So he defended himself where he could.

Of Paderewski's defense, Colonel House said, ". . . he never asked for Poland more than he thought was just or more than he thought she could digest. His recommendations to those having the deciding voice, if accepted, would have brought a fuller measure of peace, not alone to Poland, but to continental Europe as well. He saw clearly and with vision, and had the courage to combat public opinion both at home and abroad. This—always a difficult task—was especially difficult in the conditions following the World War. People were unreasoning and unreasonable.

"If a year before the Peace was made Poland had been assured one half of what was given her at Paris, her citizens would have been wild with joy. In a memorable speech before the Diet at Warsaw Paderewski had the courage to tell them this and more. This was one of his great moments. He risked his popularity in one throw, and won. Time and again he met opposition and overcame it, but each time his majority in the Diet grew less." [1]

During these next torturing weeks he tried to see the straight road. After giving years to win a position of usefulness to his country, should he, to prevent civil strife, step aside? Should he leave, in the belief that with time present confusion would clear up and Poland would go ahead with her right development?

Then suddenly, on November twenty-seventh, Paderewski was struck as by a thunder-bolt. Word that he had resigned from the government spread throughout the capital. He rushed to the Assembly Chamber to deny the lie, and saw dissension everywhere. Men implored him not to let himself be forced out by dastardly means. Poland would be lost; she faced only disaster if Pilsudski were given a free hand.

There were a few more weeks of bewilderment and heartbreak; his country had turned against him. How many men, rising above personal bitterness and humiliation, would have refused, as he did, to ask if it would not be better for *himself* if he went back to his farm in Switzerland? But would ask only, "Would this be better for Poland? Would it avoid a conflict that would damage her in the eyes of nations outside?"

Then in a stormy session, the Sejm by a slight majority gave him a vote of confidence. Other men would have claimed the victory. Paderewski probed it. His next action was startling, as it would be today in our Congress.

[1] From "Paderewski, the Paradox of Europe," *Harper's Magazine*, December 1925.

Representatives of all parties but two had voted for him; representatives of the Socialist and Peasant parties voted against him. The Peasant Party, led by powerful Wincenty Witos, was made up of small farmers and rural workers who formed a majority of Poland's population. Therefore, Paderewski held that even though their representatives in the Sejm were not numerous enough to defeat him, their vote meant that a citizens' majority did not support him. He believed that in a democracy the wish of the majority must be followed. On December 5, 1919, he resigned as prime minister and minister of foreign affairs.

Political supporters who practiced the "rules of the game" bitterly blamed him for this "impractical act of a high-minded artist." It took a long time (as it would today) for men to grasp the principles by which he lived, to understand a character so untouched by personal ambition. But experience taught them, one by one. It taught Witos, who, fifteen years later (himself then a political exile), during a visit to Riond Bosson, confessed that the greatest blunder of his political life had been failure to understand Paderewski's plan for the rebuilding of Poland, and his own fateful siding with the forces that opposed him.

A frightened Sejm begged Paderewski to reconsider. He remained firm. They appealed to him to stay at least long enough to form a new Cabinet. This he agreed to do; and, free of rancor, still giving his best, he met with and advised them. Then, as twenty thousand marchers converged on his hotel to present him with a memorial signed by over a hundred thousand citizens, little more than a year after he had arrived, he left Warsaw forever.

Men of vision across the world paid tribute to the courage of this renunciation. The words of two Americans, House and Hoover, express their common thought.

Colonel House wrote: "No country ever needed the services of one of her sons more than Poland needed those of Paderewski then, but he was never one of those who feel themselves indispensable. Had he been more ambitious and less patriotic and unselfish, he might have continued in power and become an autocrat." [2]

And Herbert Hoover said: "It was with rare moral courage that he made this momentous decision, without complaining, refusing to take advantage of the military arm that could have preserved him and his colleagues in office. This he did lest he should do infinite harm to the cause of democracy." [3]

[2] From "Paderewski the Paradox of Europe," *Harper's Magazine*, December 1925.

[3] "This statement was confirmed recently by Mr. Hoover."—Dr. Witold Swarokowski, Curator, Polish and Western European collections of the Hoover Library, Stanford University.

PART THREE

CHAPTER XIX

Home Again at Riond Bosson

A GRAPH drawing of Paderewski's life would show advance by clean-cut decisions, which allowed no time for regret or complaint, only time for moving forward. Now his decision seemed to lead to inaction—and should, his friends thought, watching his haggard face. The terrific struggle over, he realized that for weeks his sister's letters had lain practically unread. Five years had passed since he had left her in charge of Riond Bosson!

Sylwin Strakacz and his wife Aniela were going along; they had become indispensable family members. A staggering number of suitcases, satchels, and boxes, were piling up, but nobody worried about frontier delays because customs officers everywhere passed all Paderewski luggage without inspection, proud to have a part in expediting his trip. When he arrived at Morges, flags were flying and citizens crowding to meet the train; this had been a long separation. Others waited before Riond Bosson. At the gate Paderewski shook hands with each of his workmen and servants, then walked eagerly toward the house. Antonina was running to meet him; as they embraced, she said joyously, "No matter how it came about, it's good you're back at last!" looking up at the worn face. "You'll rest!" He kissed her cheeks and said,

"Yes, it's good." Madame Helena broke in, and there was a hearty embrace; the new family members were introduced, and Paderewski went inside. Before going upstairs he spent silent minutes in Alfred's room off the terrace; it was filled with flowers, and Alfred's wheel chair and writing table were undisturbed.

At first Paderewski was too tired even to look at the lake-side acres, the hothouses heavy with winter fruits, the animal pens. But his wife went at once to her chicken yards; she wouldn't rest until she established in some Polish city an agricultural school with experimental quarters as good as these. Like her husband, she was incapable of fixing her thoughts on personal wrongs; they still centered on Poland's needs. Gradually he returned to the old rounds, while his dogs at his heels thirstily drank in the good air. He had been home scarcely a week when the invasion of visitors began—Poles, for whom there could be no other leader, colleagues at the Peace Conference, friends from countries toured in concert days. Antonina groaned as she saw the house becoming a hotel again. She was worried, too, about her brother's finances; after pouring nearly everything he had into Poland, how could he go on in this way? But if he wouldn't change this habit of fantastic hospitality, she'd try to live up to it, but without allowing people to impose on him.

One never understood how the not very large dining room seated so many. It was a magical experience to sit at this table, the master at its head, happy in offering friends delicacies of his own growing. Polish cooks rival French chefs; their jellied fish and meats and exquisite sauces, their fabulous desserts, are a feast for the eye as well as the palate. The important two o'clock luncheon lasted two or three hours. When guests rose, following an old Polish custom, their host moved around the table, greeting each, as he had when they sat down. This interval, with witty stories and the lively conversation he believed should accompany eating (usually politics and music were taboo), highlighted the day. No matter how one might feel, there must be no gloom at table; he disliked even the wearing of black dresses. After coffee, some joined him in a game of bridge, or, if his program demanded, he climbed the stairs to his study.

All this did not mean that Paderewski had cut himself off from Poland; he followed events there with intense anxiety. And, though an exile, he kept his major posts in the international field; was still a member of the Supreme Council of the Allies; delegate to the Peace Conference, which continued to meet to iron out complications in the treaty decisions; and Poland's head delegate to the League of Nations at Geneva. His suspense was all but unbearable when Pilsudski launched an offensive in the east, and, after taking Kiev, was thrown back and forced to conduct one of the most desperate retreats in history. Paderewski saw his country's very existence, and with it a free Europe, threatened as the huge Bolshevik Army rolled on toward Warsaw. Poland had sent her prime minister to beg the Allies to beg for munitions, soldiers, and money; but they refused to act unless Paderewski represented Poland. Then the Riond Bosson telephone rang; from Warsaw the minister of foreign affairs asked Paderewski to hurry to Paris as Poland's representative to appeal for immediate aid. Without a trace of bitterness over the way this government had treated him, or any feeling of triumph as it now turned to him, he took the train. This was in July 1920; on the twenty-second he was in Paris, with headquarters at the Ritz Hotel, which had reserved its second floor for him and his family. At the hesitant Allies meeting, he argued with such fire and logic that even Lloyd George, who had been quick to say, "I told you so—they have brought this on themselves," was again won over; and at once supplies and a force under the French General Maxime Weygand were sent. He joined the heroic effort of a terrified people and, though the Bolsheviks were within six miles of Warsaw, together they saved Poland. But for Paderewski, this help might have come too late.

Poles love a story of the turning point of the battle for Warsaw, which shows a priest-scoutmaster, when the enemy was almost inside the city, holding high the crucifix under a rain of bullets as he led schoolboys in an attack which stopped the advance—a heroic action known since as the "Miracle of the Vistula." With countless others inside and outside Poland, Paderewski thanked God for this "miraculous" action of the priest-scoutmaster and his boys.

Another danger had passed; people breathed again. Paderewski believed that if the Allies had permitted him (when earlier he asked them to) to come to an agreement with Russia, this frightful new war might have been avoided. He believed this; yet he was practical, and he continued to work with them on their own terms to help Poland.

His presence in Paris was always a heralded event. People crowded the Ritz Hotel corridors to get a glimpse of him; others invented ways of winning an invitation to dinner.

Between sessions of the Supreme Council and the Peace Conference (one of these took him to Aix-les-Bains for three weeks) there was always something going on in his hotel apartment. The climax of almost four months' entertaining was a banquet for two hundred in honor of Marshal Foch, which he gave shortly before returning to Switzerland.

He reached Riond Bosson in time for the November fifteenth opening session of the League of Nations. The forty-mile run to Geneva is along an incomparable road; on the right are rolling hills, on the left snow-capped Mont Blanc and a panorama of alps rising beyond the lake. But it was more convenient to live in the city during the meeting, so he engaged a floor of the Mont Blanc Hotel for himself and his aides. When he took his place in the League's great assembly room, the world's representatives rose as one in tribute to the spirit of good will that radiated from him. They praised his action when, during Poland's bitter dispute with Lithuania, he refused to let this situation affect his attitude toward the Lithuanian delegate to the League, whom he treated as a friend.

On December fourth, when he was scheduled to make his major address, long before the hour all standing room had been taken. Few of those listening spellbound while he spoke—without notes, without an interpreter, following the French version with an identical one in English—had any conception of the work behind the perfection of this performance. They did not see him forgetting meals and sleep as he concentrated on organizing what he wanted to say, the progress from climax to climax, the search for a phrase that would more precisely express his thought, till at last he set

down the final draft in Polish, then made duplicate transla-
tions and memorized each, word by word.

Thus he gave his best to the League, though the refusal
of the United States to join it had shaken his faith in its
power to bridge the gulfs of the postwar world. And before
long he felt once more that it would be easier for his country if he withdrew from representing her officially. Often
his views lacked support at home; often they were attacked.
Wouldn't it be better if a Pole living in Poland served as its
delegate? He decided it would be, and thereafter sat in the
gallery as listener instead of on the floor. Again, there was no
fuzziness in his position; there was a clear decision, a clear
action.

He kept in touch with the personal struggle, the failing
health, of his friend Woodrow Wilson who had dedicated
his whole being to the effort to make men see that the world
brotherhood set forth in the Fourteen Points could be at-
tained.

As the immensity of his task became clearer, neighbors
of the Wilson's house on S Street in Washington could see
his body breaking under its burden. There is a little balcony
above the entrance door where he appeared as long as he
was able to when a crowd gathered below on his birthday
or on other special days. As month followed tragic month
and people looked up at the drawn, suffering face, they knew
that Woodrow Wilson was literally giving his life to that
better world which he saw. No one realized this more deeply,
or more sadly than Paderewski.

And now a factor which some might call unfortunate but
which was actually fortunate influenced Paderewski's course.

This was financial need. The millions he had made were spent; his charities, and his wife's, must continue. He could not, would not, change his scale of living: Riond Bosson's doors must remain open. These were not small sums that he needed, and he saw only one way to find them, the way that had brought the earlier fortunes. He had dreamed of coming home at last to give his remaining years to composing. How many times he had felt that the opportunity to write music had at last come, when suddenly his country's need, or some other human need, blocked the way—as it did today.

When he thought of the piano he had closed (except for a few relief programs) more than five years ago, he was painfully conscious of stiff muscles in fingers, hands, arms, and feet. At his age could a man start a new concert career? The world would say "No." But the old confidence flared; he said, "Perhaps." To play again meant building from the ground up: brain and muscles must put on the old harness. He wondered if he would be equal to such concentrated work over a period of time; before he could know, he must restore a worn-out body. His best chance to do this lay, he felt, in the sunshine and waters of Paso Robles Hot Springs near his farm in California. On his previous visits these sulphur baths had relieved a very painful neuritis.

Again Antonina was left in charge of Riond Bosson. He and Madame Paderewska, Sylwin Strakacz, his wife Aniela, and another loved member of the "family," Helena Liibke, started for California. The last hours were hectic; the inevitable mountains of packages and suitcases piled up in front of the house, including one made specially for Ping, Madame Paderewska's Pekingese, a problem on trains and in hotels.

She had the required permissions, but even so, it seemed safer to conceal Ping. On the final lap of the journey they visited San Francisco, which Paderewski tried never to miss. Among its excitements was Chinatown, where he was pretty sure to uncover beautiful objects to add to his Chinese collection, and where he could listen with delight to the theaters' Chinese orchestras.

They reached Paso Robles at night, to find the whole countryside illuminated. Big cities weren't the only ones who knew how to welcome a great man! Aniela Strakacz's diary notes glow as she tells how this little western town received them. Citizens crowded to the station, where each became a welcoming committee member and seized a package or bag, while the Paderewskis were escorted to an open car between two long lines of others bearing torches. Facing their open car, a company of little girls marched backward, scattering flowers, and to the time of music played by motor horns, the slow, proud procession moved toward the hotel.

Paderewski was first attracted to Paso Robles, with its golden oak-dotted hills, because Modjeska once tried to establish a Polish colony there; though it failed to develop, her plan led many Poles to settle in Southern California. In 1913 Ignace Paderewski had bought a farm of twenty-six hundred acres in the beautiful hill section that borders on the village. He named the farm Ignatio, after his patron saint, and planted it with vineyards and almond, walnut, and prune orchards. In spite of an unlucky choice of managers which several times threatened to ruin him he loved the property and always enjoyed renewing there his friendship with the former country doctor who ran the Hot Springs

Hotel. Though this doctor was an insistent promoter of Paso Robles properties, he was so steeped in the Spanish tradition that made the rich background of the region that the two men used to talk for hours, tramping back and forth under fruit trees. Paderewski now decided that he should feel as much at home in Spanish as in other languages, and began to study it; later, in Switzerland, he drove to a nearby city five mornings a week for lessons.

In this quiet town movies were a chief diversion. Paderewski sometimes went to them twice a day, and, no matter what the picture, followed it with a childlike absorption and enjoyment and came away relaxed and refreshed. One of the family's preparations for going to the show was a bit of a show in itself, for Ping wasn't supposed to enter the theater, and, since Madame Paderewska wouldn't leave her pet at home, he had, each time, to be silenced and innocently transported in a steamer rug.

The tired man had counted on Paso Robles to start him on the hard road back to the concert stage, but as he prepared to return to Riond Bosson he knew that only after many more months of build-up and of terrific work could he hope to succeed.

CHAPTER XX

"The Great Return"

AFTER a year and a half of preparation, Paderewski was committed to the great venture. To worried friends he said, "You know, energy feeds on activity." When he sailed from New York in the middle of 1922, he announced that he would return to give a concert in Carnegie Hall on November twenty-second.

Wires sent out this promise as a top news item, a sporting event. He was sixty-two. For five years he had been a world figure in politics, the musician silenced; now he challenged that musician to reconquer the concert stage. The press was right; their flash thrilled people in every state. Many doubted, but all wanted him to win.

None more intensely wanted him to win than did a widely scattered company of music students to whom he had given friendship and often the practical help of criticism, or piano lessons. As one of these Americans, later known as the concert pianist Elenore Altman, recalled many incidents of her lesson hours, somehow she saw first a seemingly lesser picture. Her last lesson at Riond Bosson was over, the master had come with her to the door, helped her with her coat, and put on his summer hat of soft Panama straw, the mass of ruddy hair escaping all round its rather wide brim. As they stood silently in the doorway, suddenly, with a twinkle in his eyes, he lifted the hat from his head and placed it on hers. "A lesser incident? But doesn't it," she asked, "tell one of the reasons why countless people are waiting, hoping, for Paderewski to win?"

Insurance companies, formerly so eager to insure his tours but who today refused to take the risk, were staggered by the spectacle of Carnegie Hall on November twenty-second —by the sight of an audience literally battling its way in, then rising to its feet with tremendous applause as the beloved pianist stepped onto the platform, fighting a nervousness which luckily they could not see. The careful insurance agents had failed to take into account the delight of thousands as the marvelous program progressed; of their refusal to leave the hall even after encores which amounted to the length of the original concert; of their refusal still to go when lights were turned off. Already wires were carrying the report of the victory of the good, the great man, the transcendent artist. Someone said that Paderewski's triumph was hailed by a cry of joy across the country.

There were those who found technical flaws in his playing not present a half-dozen years earlier, but this criticism was lost in the comment of leading musical critics. Their praise read like a contest in superlatives.

On this first tour of the Return he played in twenty-three cities and earned about half a million dollars. He again lived in his private car and slept in railway yards undisturbed by the bells and switching, pleased if yardmen listened when he practiced. This was a life he loved—strenuous, yes, but he did not practice as many hours as formerly. He got better results now from a few hours' continuous work than from any such fourteen-hour stretches as he had been accustomed to in his earlier years. And no matter how pressed, he still found time for the unexpected incident that starred the day, time to talk about their faraway relatives with little Polish girls who brought him flowers; to run his car from Phoenix, where he played, down to Tucson so that two boys at school there could spend three hours with him and he could report the visit to their mother in New York; to play a special program for a group of nuns unable to come to his concert; to see that an eleven-year-old boy, who hadn't the price of a ticket, got one plus a visit and an autograph after the concert.

But though Paderewski's habitual attitude was one of warmth and good will, he could be quick to make his displeasure felt when offended. He disliked persons who spoke of their sorrows in public, or who, after failure, had not the will to fight on. Once at Riond Bosson he said to his sister in a whisper that sounded across the dining room, "That man must never be invited here again." And he never was.

In Europe the Return was another progress from ovation to ovation, with kings and queens joining the man from the street to honor him. The comment carried by a Brussels paper pleased him most because it turned the praise to Poland: "Only a heroic people could produce the miracle of such a man."

And now he was able to carry out a plan which was extremely important to him. He wanted in a practical action to express again his gratitude to Herbert Hoover and other Americans who had saved starving Poles, by turning over the proceeds of a concert series to unemployed Americans.

He asked Mrs. Hoover, then in the White House, to sponsor the series. After the initial one, in Washington, where he was a guest of the President and his wife, Mrs. Hoover wrote to Red Cross Chairman John Barton Payne, "Enclosed please find a check for eleven thousand, eight hundred and fifty-two dollars and seventy cents which was sent me by Mr. Paderewski for the benefit of the unemployed of our country. May I mention in passing that Mr. Paderewski especially wanted it to purchase food for Americans hungry and in distress so if you can see that it quite certainly goes for that purpose we will be carrying out the wish of the generous donor."

Paderewski kept constantly in mind, too, not only Poland's soldiers, but the Allies' soldiers who had fought for Poland, and undertook to repay part of that debt by pouring a large part of his new earnings into soldiers' hospitals. Often he gave special benefit concerts for them. It would be hard to chart fully all his effort to return kindness by kindness. He gave to Marshal Foch's widow two million francs for her war-relief work—all the net proceeds of a tour in the French provinces. He was the largest individual contributor to the American Legion's endowment fund for disabled veterans, and was the only civilian foreigner made an honorary member of the Legion. Outstanding was a recital in France for Jewish refugees from Germany. But climaxing all additions to his regular schedule was the benefit on February 8, 1932, in New York's vast, barnlike Madison Square Garden, for unemployed musicians.

To many of those who were there Lawrence Gilman's account in the New York *Herald Tribune* the following morning not only gives a true picture of the performance, and especially of Paderewski's spiritual communion with his audience, but is at the same time an interpretation of all his major performances across the long span of years. Mr. Gilman wrote:

Before an audience vaster than any recitalist had ever faced, the Grand Seigneur of music, who happens also to be one of the first citizens of the world, played the piano last evening at Madison Square Garden for the benefit of unemployed musicians. In an environment hallowed by memories of championship bouts and prize airedales and trick elephants, Mr. Paderewski discoursed of Beethoven and Schubert and Chopin.

An audience that drew its members not only from the Social Register and Who's Who in Music, but from thousands who had probably never heard a recital by the most illustrious of living virtuosi, filled the Garden almost to capacity—the official record of attendance was 16,000. The receipts were approximately $33,500. To speak of the mounting enthusiasm, of the many added numbers, would be superfluous. . . .

Mr. Paderewski played on a stage built across the west end of the Garden, with a sounding-board at the back, and a yellow silk curtain shutting off the space behind. The sixteen thousand listeners filled the rows of seats in the arena, the boxes, and the tiers at the sides and the east end. Even in the upper places farthest from the stage, the piano's sound, unaided by amplifiers, was clearly audible. . . .

But even more impressive than the spectacle and the sound of the lone, absorbed interpreter on his darkened platform, making music for an audience of unprecedented immensity, was the stillness of the listeners—many of them a block away from the stage. For long moments—as during the performance of the Chopin Sonata—it was difficult to believe that there were any hearers present save one's immediate neighbors; and again one realized that the casting of spells is still occasionally possible. Even in a standardized and mechanistic world, genius continues to be magical and sovereign and inescapable. . . .

Like most interpretive artists of inflammable imagination and spiritual capaciousness, Mr. Paderewski has the faculty of rising to the level of great occasions, aesthetic or broadly human; the ability to give most when most is needed. The implications of last night's occasion must have stirred deeply his sensitive sympathies and his vivid imagination; and perhaps he was not unaware, simple and modest though he is, of the extraordinary atmosphere of veneration and affection which surrounded him, the quickening currents of responsiveness generated by that enormous throng who hung upon every movement of his fingers and were held by every nuance that they evoked. . . .

Mr. Paderewski has often seemed to be in revolt against the natural limitations of the piano, as if he would compel its throat to be an orchestra's, myriad-voiced and thunderous. But last evening he was perhaps most unforgettably personal when he disclosed himself as intimately in harmony with his medium, accepting and sublimating its limitations— in, for example, his exquisite voicing of Chopin's cantilena in the slow movement of the Sonata.

Who else can play Chopin with Paderewski's flame-edged grace, his blend of fire and tenderness, his superb distinction of style? Who else can discourse to us with those strange accessions of divine madness that seize upon this uncompanioned artist when he is at his most subduing? . . .

But chiefly, and most restoringly, what one acquires from an experience of Mr. Paderewski's playing is the conviction that one has been in contact with a noble and kindled and insuperable spirit. If, last evening, he seemed more than usually puissant and moving, perhaps it was because he shared the thoughts that were provoked by the occasion and by his own deep intimacy with its mood and impulse—as if, with one here and there among his listeners, he may have remembered Whitman's meditation: "I look out upon all the sorrows of the world . . . All the meannesses and agony without end: I, sitting, look out upon, see, hear, and am silent."

Silence, declared the subtlest of modern thinkers many years ago, is the supreme revealer—of wisdom, of revelation: "The reservoirs of silence," he wrote, "lie far above the reservoirs of thought." But the reservoirs of music lie higher still.

Paderewski's wife did not see this spectacle; her illness had progressed so far that she could no longer leave her apartment at Riond Bosson. He had lost his only son, and now this slow darkening tragedy. Between tours he spent much time in her room, sitting quietly holding her hand, trying to reach across mental oblivion. If she recognized him, his happiness was written on his face when he rejoined the family group below. He was with her when she died in January 1934.

Between concerts he was often asked to speak, to explain the "Polish situation" to baffled Americans. He welcomed these opportunities, especially since they gave him a chance to express gratitude to America. Not long after an emergency

operation (at seventy-one) for a ruptured appendix, that
held him in a Lausanne hospital for three months, he
gave in New York such a clear, forceful explanation of the
complicated Polish Corridor question that Americans who
knew little about northeastern Europe or the reasons why
Poland, to live, must have an outlet to the sea, felt they understood this necessity.

He worked long and hard on this speech, seizing time between programs to organize its great body of detail. When
he finished, it was as beautifully built as one of his musical
compositions. Because of the seriousness of the argument, he
started off in light vein by telling an amusing story, then
amid laughter began his analysis. Listeners leaned forward,
asking themselves, as they had when he spoke in San Francisco, how a historical review could be so vivid, stirring.
When he spoke of America they were as intensely moved
as they had been when in an earlier speech he said, "I found
here friends, many good friends, who most generously en-
abled me to collect funds for the relief of our war victims.
. . . Then your Herbert Hoover, our Herbert Hoover, en-
deavored to bring into Poland your aid needed by our
hunger-stricken people. . . . Let me incline my head with
profound reverence and infinite gratitude before the sanctity
and greatness of that spirit of American idealism that re-
stored to the Polish plough the ancient soil of my forefa-
thers . . . that American idealism which is expressed in the
sacred symbol of your young nation, the Stars and Stripes,
in the folds of which we have found at last, hidden for over
a hundred years, the independence of Poland." [1]

[1] From The Corridor Speech made at a testimonial dinner to

Thus, tour by tour, he approached the end of the 1930s and the end of the Return. Then he sailed for Europe. The little family circle at Riond Bosson who saw his magnificent vitality ebbing were terribly concerned when he insisted on going back to the United States for just one more series of concerts. At Philadelphia, from the crowded stage, packed galleries seemed to form a single pulsating curtain that fell from ceiling to floor. Old and young (grandparents had brought their grandchildren that they might remember him) sat close and still, thinking that this would be his final concert there. Those near the Steinway who saw the beads of sweat run down the gray cheeks realized the price he was paying as once more he lifted and freed men. When it was over many pushed toward the piano to touch it, feeling that through this action they could somehow touch the power that had struck shackles from their souls.

He reached the small backstage room with difficulty; yet as he stood there silently a few minutes, the tide of creative energy, not yet spent, seemed still to course through his frail body, channel of the eternal, all-uniting flow.

Three weeks later the thousands who packed Madison Square Garden waited anxiously as the clock ticked on from the opening hour (eight-thirty) to eight-forty-five. Front pages of the next morning's newspapers explained the waiting: "Paderewski collapses at Garden as fifteen thousand gather for a concert. Suffers slight heart attack in dressing room. Other engagements are canceled. Dr. Theodore

---

Paderewski, New York, May 6, 1928. Printed on p. 9 of *Ignace Jan Paderewski, 1918–1928*, issued by the Kosciuszko Foundation, New York.

Dunham, his private physician, and Sylwin Strakacz sped Mr. Paderewski to his private car on Track 31 in the Grand Central Terminal . . ." Meanwhile the audience, which included many notables of the musical world, heard in stunned silence the Garden's loud-speaker announcement. Some burst into tears and were still weeping as they left the auditorium. Shortly afterward, men went about suggesting that purchasers of tickets leave what they had paid at the box office to start a fund to be turned over to Mr. Paderewski as a token of affection and esteem. Thus the final Return closed. Five days later he had recovered sufficiently to sail for Europe. If he could have foreseen the pattern of the next few months, would he have sailed?

CHAPTER XXI

World War II. Flight from Europe to New York

AFTER a month of treatment with a Paris doctor, a frail Paderewski once again came home to Riond Bosson, this time for absolute rest. Yet who could rest in July and August of 1939 with their daily mounting fear of war? Paderewski had never listened to the radio, but the family kept close to it, and on September first Strakacz, pale and shaken, hurried to the president's study. Germany had invaded Poland, war had begun. Paderewski heard the news in silence; all he had helped to create would be blown to dust.

The expert Swiss who for a century had held their land neutral in the midst of war, began mobilizing at once, choosing Riond Bosson as round-up center for cavalry of that region. Lawns and orchards were trampled by men and their beautiful horses; but though fruit trees were heavy with apples and pears, true to Swiss practice, not one was taken, no tree harmed. Within five days, England and France declared war on Germany; in Poland hope rose, only to fall when twelve days later Russia, breaking a non-aggression

pact, struck from the east. Thus World War II, with its be-
trayal of man's highest aspiration, spread.

Thousands of Poles, young and old, left everything behind and fled southward to try to cross the Rumanian frontier before it became more tightly sealed. The American ambassador, Anthony Drexel Biddle, and Paul Super, American
head of the Polish Y.M.C.A., pushed on with them, giving
aid. In the United States, chiefly because of the "love bank"
Paderewski had built here, a national Polish Relief Committee was quickly formed with President Henry Noble Mc-
Cracken of Vassar College as chairman. The love bank paid
dividends immediately. A first ten thousand dollars, cabled
to the American Legation at Bucharest, arrived just as Ambassador Biddle and Paul Super did, with five dollars left
between them. Super began setting up a chain of relief stations across Rumania for the stream of foodless, shoeless
refugees heading west through Hungary to France. Escaping, too, were President Raczkiewicz and General Sikorski;
in Paris they would re-establish the Polish government.

Inside Poland and outside, Poles and their allies looked to
one Pole to lead them; he was seventy-nine, his health was
shattered; but no one stood as he. Daily, soldiers, civilians,
and officials managed to reach Morges to beg for advice. On
September twenty-first General Sikorski arrived, en route
to France. When he and Paderewski met neither could
speak; then Sikorski painfully told what had happened so
far; he outlined his plan to continue the Polish government
in Paris under President Raczkiewicz, with a Polish National
Council to take the place of parliament, and with Paderewski
as prime minister. Paderewski knew that he could not accept

this post; he insisted that Sikorski undertake it. But he agreed to travel to Paris to help inaugurate the new government, and to act as one of the committee of three (Raczkiewicz, Sikorski, and himself) whose decisions would determine policy.

The following January, 1940, he taxied across blacked-out Paris to a heatless hotel, and two days later to the Polish Embassy for the inaugural ceremony. He had worked all night for several nights on his address which would express to all peoples the faith and aims of an unconquerable Poland. At its climax the audience in the packed Embassy room was on its feet listening. He was calling now to those inside Poland:

"Across the trench lines, across the land of our foes, my voice speeds on toward you, bringing steadfast faith in your strength, faith in the inflexibility of our sacred rights to our land, faith in ultimate victory. That voice cannot be silenced by the barbarous oppressor because it lives in the soul of each one of you. That profound faith in God and in Poland gives you the strength to survive the period of bondage and will permit you to live to see the day of our ultimate joint triumph." [1]

There was breathless silence; heads were bowed as in prayer. Then there was thunderous applause, as Paderewski sank heavily into an armchair.

He returned to Riond Bosson. Strakacz was to commute between it and Paris as his representative with the new

[1] *Paderewski as I Knew Him*, by Aniela Strakacz, translated by Halina Chybowska. New Brunswick, New Jersey: Rutgers University Press, 1949.

government. Again, from the famous study, letters and wires poured out to the continents. Paderewski had sent a long message to India's Gandhi, preacher of non-violence, asking him to give his moral support to the Poles. He had not met Gandhi, but in all periods of history there are families of great spirits who recognize one another across frontiers of space and time. Gandhi's reply made him happy, as did his public statement: "Of course, my whole heart is with the Poles in the unequal struggle in which they are engaged for the sake of saving their freedom. I send to the brave Poles my heartfelt prayer for the early termination of their fearful trial and for the grant of the required strength to bear the suffering whose very contemplation makes one shudder." [2]

This utterance showed that India, though engaged in a desperate struggle to win her own freedom from Britain, would support Britain as she tried to help Poland.

Then came the staggering blow: French Premier Pétain gave up, asked Hitler for an armistice. This meant the fall of France, the flight of the new Polish government to England.

Paderewski, foreseeing, as he had in World War I, America's entry into World War II, felt that he could now better accomplish his task from the United States, and decided to return. There were signs that Hitler's agents might prevent his going even as far as France. If he was to get to Spain and thence to Portugal he must act before the whole of France was lost. This time his sister would go; his friend and valet, Franciszek; and Sylwin and Aniela Strakacz with their daughter Anette. His secretary, the alert young Pole, Ignace Kollupailo, was to join them at the French frontier. That

[2] *Paderewski as I Knew Him,* by Aniela Strakacz.

made seven passengers with their combined luggage for two cars, the Cadillac that Herbert Hoover had presented to Paderewski in Warsaw, and another less good. Departure was a scramble; so few possessions could go, so many friends were still surging into the house for a last-minute word. But finally they were starting. Paderewski (did he suspect that he would never see this home, these friends, again?) shook hands gravely with each servant and guest, and the overloaded cars rolled out to the road. The sad group watching them disappear asked one another if Hitler would not indeed prevent Paderewski's reaching the United States.

Aniela Strakacz's story of the family's historic flight to Lisbon, the only possible sailing port, reads like a movie thriller: the maneuvering under protection of an agent of the French security police, across France, which the enemy was taking over section by section; miraculous escapes in storms on Spain's mountain roads. Toward Barcelona they ran into hurricane winds and cloudbursts that turned day into night; at times they could proceed only when lightning showed the mountains on one side and the sea below. Then slowly the first car would hurdle washouts, ford torrents, and wind through a litter of ripped branches, and the Cadillac with Paderewski and his sister followed. Everyone else was worrying about them, but they took the experience calmly, and finally got rest in Barcelona.

The next day's seven-hour trip to Saragossa was again a hard one; Paderewski needed a good night's rest before continuing to Madrid. But at Saragossa the travelers were met by police agents, taken to the police station, and ordered to return at once to Barcelona! When they demanded the meaning of this action they were told mysteriously that it was taken because of concern for Mr. Paderewski's safety. Then began Strakacz' singled-handed battle with the police and their masters. He refused to go back, threatened Spain with world condemnation if it brought harm to one hair of Paderewski's head. The loud battle inside raged for an hour and a half, while the principal character in the plot sat outside in the Cadillac.

Strakacz won the first round. The party was under arrest, but could stay "for one night only" at the Gran Hotel; at eight in the morning, they must go back to Barcelona. Strakacz' last shot was, "In all his life Mr. Paderewski has never started on a trip at eight o'clock in the morning!" They proceeded under guard to the Gran, where the two cars and their possessions were sealed and taken back to the police station. Strakacz had not been allowed to telephone the Polish Legation in Madrid; now he requested the hotel to forward his wires to the Polish Minister, the British Ambassador, and the American Ambassador, Mr. Weddell. They didn't dare refuse, but no one could be sure that Madrid would deliver them. Already the American press was blazoning the news, "Paderewski Kidnaped!" Morning and evening an anxious public searched for reports from the Gran Hotel. Meanwhile he was calmly playing cards inside and laughing at his sister's black prediction that they were headed for a concentration camp where Hitler would hold them till the war ended.

It was Ambassador Weddell's wire to President Roosevelt —who cabled General Franco asking that his personal friend, Paderewski, be freed to proceed—that brought an end to this fantastic episode and a message from Weddell inviting the great Pole to rest in Madrid at the American Embassy before going on to the Lisbon boat. To this Paderewski replied:

DEEPLY TOUCHED BY YOUR MOST KIND INVITATION TO BE YOUR GUEST AT THE EMBASSY STOP I REGRET BEING DEPRIVED OF THE HONOR OF ACCEPTING YOUR GENEROUS HOSPITALITY STOP MY SISTER AND SEVERAL FRIENDS ARE TRAVELLING WITH ME AND WE HAVE ALREADY MADE RESERVATIONS IN MADRID STOP I WISH TO EXPRESS TO YOU MY WARMEST THANKS FOR THE KIND INTEREST YOU HAVE TAKEN IN MY EXTRAORDINARY ADVENTURE WITH THE SPANISH POLICE AND AM EXTREMELY GRATEFUL FOR YOUR MOST VALUABLE ASSISTANCE AND SYMPATHY STOP SINCERELY HOPE TO BE ABLE TO OFFER YOU PERSONALLY MY RESPECTFUL REGARDS ONCE PERMITTED TO LEAVE SARAGOSSA FOR MADRID   PADEREWSKI.[3]

The following day (the sixth after their arrival at Saragossa) they did leave; but now there was a third car, an escort from the American Embassy. In Madrid there were a great number of German officers on the streets. Had they or others in Barcelona, been given a Hitler assignment which they weren't able to carry out?

One month after the flight from Riond Bosson travelers boarded a small boat in Lisbon bound for New York. Soon boat drill was called, and someone, seeing Paderewski's difficulty in putting on the bulky life preserver, objected, "But surely you aren't expected to go through with this?" "Everybody means everybody," he replied, and with a little help managed to fasten the belt.

[3] Drawn from *Paderewski as I Knew Him*, by Aniela Strakacz.

CHAPTER XXII

Death

No matter how circumstances changed, the pattern of Paderewski's inner life remained unchanged. In New York he continued to give an ebbing strength for Poland; he sat long at a desk writing letters, thinking out speeches; he continued to pour out his love to people about him, of whatever station in life. Among first visitors at the Ritz Tower Hotel were the colored porters, John and Charles, who for years attended him in the concert car, and Augusta, the maid who had traveled with him and Madame Paderewska. This reunion cheered him immensely, and drove away for the moment the grief with which he followed his country's daily more desperate situation.

It soon became clear that a hotel of touring days was not suited to the tired man of today; he needed a simple, less costly home, and found it at the Buckingham Hotel, in the music quarter of West Fifty-seventh Street, where a comfortable floor was turned over to the "family."

Christmas approached. They planned no festivity, but from everywhere packages began arriving, until by Christmas Eve gifts were stacked ceiling-high in the living room. Climaxing all was that from the Polish Restaurant, a typical Polish Christmas Eve supper, with Polish waiters to serve it, and an orchestra that played Polish Christmas carols. Nothing could have pleased them more than this surprise.

Paderewski had not yet been welcomed officially, so Mayor La Guardia was asked if he would speak, were an occasion arranged where the great man, unable to be present, would be represented by his sister, and Mr. Strakacz would read a message from him. La Guardia was eager to do this and on January seventh, at a luncheon at the Lotos Club, known to musicians the world over, before some two hundred and fifty outstanding friends, with President Wilson's under-secretary of state, Frank Polk, presiding, the mayor, with deepest feeling, expressed the happiness the beloved musician-statesman's return had brought to the people of New York and the rest of the United States.

Antonina, asked to represent her brother, was troubled. Would she be expected to make what we called a "speech"? Her first, and in English? She was eighty-three; the prospect was terrifying! "Not a speech, but perhaps you would say a few words." She tried to think it through. "Well, if I can speak just a little conversation from the heart, I will try." Friends admired this sportsmanlike acceptance of an ordeal, and were delighted with her concern about how she must look. The little fur cape, her brother's gift, and the square-cut diamond ear-drops, left to her by Madame Paderewska —luckily these had been squeezed into one of the Swiss suitcases; but a becoming hat? From the moment she stepped forward and spoke the first "words from her heart," she completely won her audience; they loved her utter lack of self-consciousness, her gallant spirit, her humor.

Winter weather and work were telling on Paderewski's

health; yet a worried doctor had failed, so far, to persuade
him to go to Florida. Persuasion might have been easier had
the doctor advised a trip to California; but that trip was too
long, too costly. Finally a villa at Palm Beach was rented.
But to keep Paderewski there—that was another matter. He
felt cut off from the work he was still dedicated to. That
he stayed until May was due to the day-to-day triumph of a
family conspiracy, chiefly to the skill of Aniela Strakacz; no
actual daughter could have been more watchful. Indeed,
Paderewski often spoke of her and Sylwin as "our daughter,"
"our son." He liked, too, to refer to his close-knit little family
as "my children." "How are my dear children today?" he
would ask.

High points of the vacation, which helped to extend it,
were his visit with Mrs. Eleanor Roosevelt, also in Florida;
the Easter arrival of General Sikorski to report the accom-
plishments and plans of the Polish government in exile; and
the National Broadcasting Company's setting up of equipment
in the villa for a coast-to-coast broadcast of America's Council of Democracy, on which Paderewski was to speak.

We have an unforgettable picture of an incident of the
Florida stay. Someone had given Aniela Strakacz' daughter a
baby alligator. "Anetka is delighted with it," her mother
wrote, "and carries it around with her, but I have an aversion
for the creature and feel like running out of the room whenever I see it. Today Anetka had the bright idea of letting
it loose on the dining table as we sat drinking our demi-tasse.
The alligator commenced its journey among the cups, paus-
ing to look around every so often. Naturally, I ran away and
sought refuge on a window seat. The President, whose habit

it is to keep his hands on the table, drumming out something or other with all five fingers, held them motionless at sight of the approching 'gator. I appealed to him to remove his hands from the table, but he left them there, inspecting the reptile the while. My heart almost stopped beating for fear the alligator might bite his hand, but a few moments later we were all staring in incredulous amazement. The alligator had moved right up to the President's hand, which didn't even quiver, pulled out a webbed foot and unmistakenly begun to stroke his fingers. Then it drew even closer, rested its tiny head against Paderewski's hand and remained motionless. This wasn't the first time I'd seen the President reveal such a strange attraction for animals." [1]

Before leaving Palm Beach, Paderewski had his only opportunity to attend one of the many hundred concerts the relief committee arranged across the United States, in Britain and Canada, and farther away, as a testimonial to him on the fiftieth anniversary of his American debut. Everywhere outstanding soloists, and orchestras contributed programs. From an armchair in a friend's villa he listened to Richard Crooks' singing, and realized that the thousands of dollars made would help his people. He had been asked to direct the use of all funds gathered.

As part of the testimonial, a Golden Anniversary Book was to be presented at the close of the year. Fortunately groups of the eloquent pages as they arrived were taken to the Buckingham Hotel for him to see. On one of these days his face lighted up; he took from his desk a two-dollar bill. "This came to me personally yesterday for the work," he

[1] *Paderewski as I Knew Him*, by Aniela Strakacz.

said. Could it be—the pleasure, simple as a child's, in the eyes
of a man completely untouched by the fortunes he had made
and given? Those witnessing it felt that they were looking
into the purity of a human spirit.

New York weather was steaming hot; each day left Paderewski weaker. But no one was able to prevent his promising
to go to Oak Ridge, New Jersey, to speak at a Polish war
veterans' rally. The anxious family arranged for him to drive
in an open car and to speak from it. On the day before the
exercises came a report which made him all the more determined to go; Germany, turning on her former partner, had
attacked Russia. Anne O'Hare McCormick wrote in the
New York Times, "His country would be once more over-
run, this time by the Germans driving out the Russians Hitler
had let in. He saw Poland the victim of the bargain of the
dictators and likewise of their break. He saw his people
count less than leaves of grass in the path of ambitions as in-
human as the elements."

In spite of the heat an immense crowd had gathered at
Oak Ridge; Paderewski's car could scarcely inch forward
because of the people pressing around it. As he finished his
speech; hundreds were weeping, again trying to touch his
sleeve and kiss his hand. He asked for a glass of water. It was
a scene of indescribable emotion—and, alas, of farewell. A
week later, at about midnight on June 29, 1941, he died of
pneumonia—died as he would have wished, in harness, working almost to his last day. He had to drop that work before
he knew when and how Poland would again be freed, but his
faith that she would be was unbroken.

For some time Paderewski's family had realized that he was growing weaker; but no one guessed the end was so near. They were prostrated; they scarcely knew where to turn, in a city where suddenly everything seemed strange, especially the distant mortuary. When their hotel manager suggested that the body be brought "home" from the mortuary to remain until the cathedral service, they felt comforted and began at once to convert the living room into a chapel. But the burial place—where? Then came a message from Washington: President Roosevelt, in an action that had been taken only once before by the United States, had ordered that Paderewski be buried at Arlington Cemetery.

As soon as radio and press spread the news which "steeped the civilized world in mourning," white and red wreaths and sheaves poured into the hotel room chapel where the glass-covered casket rested before the upright piano, with its Chopin volume open at the Nocturne the master had so recently played. Day and night a continuous line of people passed silently before it.

On July fourth, press and radio accounts of the funeral service sped across continents. The *New York Times* head-lined its story: "Saint Patrick's Cathedral crowded with more than 4,500 at services for Paderewski. 35,000 outside Cathedral pay tribute as cortege proceeds down Fifth Avenue. Favorite music heard at Mass. Statesmen and leaders in music world present."

> For two hours [it continued], the Cathedral echoed the quiet voice of Archbishop Spellman, choir singing, and organ music which included Paderewski's favorite pieces

and his own Nocturne. Flickering lights of six large candles
fell across the white and red of the Polish flag and the design of the white eagle woven on its center, which draped
the casket near the altar rail.

As the coffin was borne through the big doors on Fifth
Avenue, about noon, a military band from Fort Jay gave
four flourishes of drums and trumpets, the highest honor
possible, and struck up the Polish national anthem, while
four hundred soldiers of the American guard of honor stood
at attention on Fifth Avenue.

The coffin was placed upon the caisson drawn by six
horses, with three outriders and the funeral procession of
nearly two thousand started for Pennsylvania Station, soldiers marching with massed colors.

About ten thousand persons crowded into the streets
around the Cathedral; another fifteen thousand watched reverently as the cortege turned west; another ten thousand
gathered at the station. Three automobiles at the end of the
procession were filled with flowers. During the march the
army band played the Dead March from Saul by Handel,
and Chopin's Funeral March.

At the station the coffin and flowers were placed aboard
the private car in which Paderewski had made his farewell
concert tour in the United States—another carried the
mourners—and attached to the Washington-bound Colonial
Express. In the national capital the body will lie in state at
the Polish Embassy until tomorrow when the burial at
Arlington will take place.

There were like headlines in Washington: "Paderewski
rests with heroes of the U.S. Temporary burial under mast
of battleship *Maine*, at Arlington. Notables pay homage.

Mrs. Woodrow Wilson present. Throngs of plain Americans also at funeral."

When the caisson bearing the body of Paderewski passed the marble entrance of the cemetery a battery of cannon boomed a nineteen-gun salute, the highest honor possible except for a chief of state. After a solemn service in the amphitheater, the United States Army Band played Chopin's Funeral March and the cortege, preceded by a detachment of soldiers, sailors, and Marines, marched slowly up the hillside road. They were accompanied by a squad of Polish soldiers in the uniform of Canada. These had received special permission from the Canadian Government to go to Washington, and bore on a velvet cushion the Polish Military Cross awarded to Paderewski by the Polish government in exile. Antonina, her life-long mission from the Polish village to Arlington ended (she lived but a few months longer), walked behind the flag-covered coffin, the "family," the Polish ambassador, and many others with her. Under the mast of the battleship *Maine*, which stands in the center of the cemetery, the body was placed in a vault. There it will remain until it can be transported to a free Poland for burial.

The service was over, but people were slow to go. They stood recalling glorious hours, glad that he had come back to his loved America in time, that Americans would guard his dust. Many thought of his last Washington concert, when in a transcendent moment the hearts of thousands seemed to beat as one, as he lifted men to an overwhelming sense of the unity of being. It had been as if a part of each listener would go when he left. Encore had followed encore, until finally colored porters rolled the piano off the stage. A group still stood inside the door. Someone had asked, "Why do we wait?" Justice Harlan Fiske Stone, later chief justice, had said, "It is hard to face again a divided world. We linger not only because Paderewski is the world's greatest pianist, but because he is perhaps the greatest living man."

INDEX

INDEX